TRANSITI(

MW00667038

TRANSITIONS

PetMassage Energy Work for the Aging & Dying Dog

Jonathan Rudinger, RN LMT
Founder and Director
PetMassage™ Training and Research Institute

TRANSITIONS PetMassage Energy Work
for the Aging & Dying Dog

Jonathan Rudinger – Revised edition

Includes bibliographical references
1. Pet Care 2. Pet Grieving 3. Holistic Animal Care 4. Massage Dog 5. Pet Massage 6. Alternative Veterinary 7. Complementary and alternative medicine 8. Acupressure 9. Animal Communication 10. Dogs—Social Aspects—Anecdotes 11. Dogs—Therapeutic—Anecdotes 12. Human Animal Relationships 13. Euthanasia....14. PetMassageTM Training & Research Institute

Cover Design Jonathan Rudinger:
Back cover photo by Cheryl Hall Photography
Photographs throughout the book by Jonathan Rudinger

Visit our website at www.PetMassage.com
For information, address PetMassage BooksTM, PetMassage, Ltd.
3347 McGregor Lane, Toledo, OH 43623 USA.

Rudinger, Jonathan
PetMassage BooksTM

REVISED EDITION

ISBN 978-0-9664826-9-0

Also by Jonathan Rudinger

Effective Pet Massage for Dogs, Manual

Effective Pet Massage for Dogs, Volume 1, DVD

Effective Pet Massage for Older Dogs, Volume 2, DVD

Creating & Marketing Your Animal Massage Business, Book

PetMassageTM: Energy Work With Dogs, Accessing the Magnificent Body Language & Body Wisdom of the Dog through Acupressure, Chakras & Positional Release, Book

PetMassageTM: Energy Work With Dogs, Accessing the Magnificent Body Language & Body Wisdom of the Dog through Acupressure, Chakras & Positional Release, 5 Audio CD Set

PetMassageTM*: A Kid's Guide to Massaging Dogs*, DVD

PetMassageTM: Doggie Songs for Kids, Audio CD,
Music and lyrics by Jonathan Rudinger, performed by Charlie Oswanski

Dogs Kids PetMassage, book

Dedication

This is for all the horses, dogs, cats and other critters and their caring people that I have had the honor to connect with since I started providing massage to animals in the early 1980's. Thank you for trusting me, so that I could allow my intuition to lead me to develop the methods in the PetMassage course. Thank you to my students, some of whom are pictured throughout the book. Teaching you has helped me to question every aspect of animal massage from its efficacy to its techniques. You have helped me to face my inner guides and pay attention to their insights.

I thank you, Anastasia, my wife and guide, for maintaining your sense of humor with an obsessive writer and dreamer. Your editing and proofing talents are most appreciated. Thank you, my pal and daughter, Samantha Macke for proofing and for your organizational suggestions. Thank you to my assistant Beth Farkas. Your help and support have been essential. Thank you all for your encouragement.
-JR

Vision

I can envision a time in the very near future when we will see animal massage clinics as frequently as we see grooming shops. Soon, animal massage therapists will be integral elements of most veterinary practices as respected colleagues assisting in rehab, wellness maintenance and counseling.

Caveat
Massage is not, nor is it intended to be a substitute for traditional veterinary care. It is a complementary form of health care. The information in this text is provided for the purposes of education and supplementary care. The reader should regularly consult a veterinarian in matters relating to his or her dog's health and especially in regard to any symptoms, which may require diagnosis or medical attention. If you have any questions regarding the efficacy of any of the techniques suggested in this manual, please consult with your veterinarian or qualified animal massage practitioner.

Working with any animal involves inherent risk. While general massage techniques are all to be applied lovingly and gently, any receiver, animal or human, will react negatively to strokes that they perceive as abusive, invasive, or inappropriate.

The author and agents of *TRANSITIONS PetMassage Energy Work for the Aging & Dying Dog* assume no risk for injury incurred while learning to massage pets.

TRANSITIONS
PetMassage Energy Work
for the Aging & Dying Dog

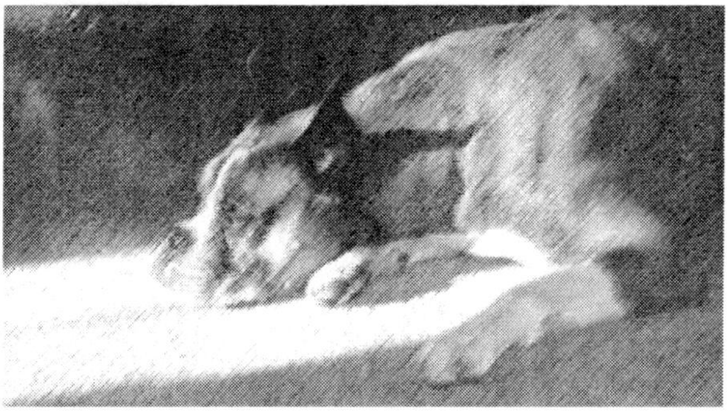

Contents

"Outside of a dog, a book is man's best friend.
Inside of a dog, it's too dark to read." - Grouch Marx

Pet•**Mas•*****'sage***
Pronunciation: 'pet, - m&-'säzh, -'säj
Function: *noun*
Etymology: **Pet** perhaps back-formation from Middle English *pety* small
1 a pampered and usually spoiled child who is treated with unusual kindness or consideration
: DARLING
2 a domesticated animal kept for pleasure rather than utility
Etymology: **Mas•sage** French, from *masser* to massage, from Arabic *massa* to stroke

Pet•**Mas•*****sage***
1 a : a form of massotherapy for animals notable for its gentleness, nurturing and support of the body's naturally powerful inclination toward balance and harmony. **PetMassage** utilizes specific skills of palpation, observation and assistive reactive movements to affect the release of fascia that may be restricting an animal's body awareness and function.
2 : more at **www.petmassage.com**

Transition
Function: *noun* Etymology: Latin *transition-, transitio,* from *transpire* Date: 1551
Passage from one state, stage, subject, or place to another: **CHANGE** A movement, development, or evolution from one form, stage, or style to another. An abrupt change in energy state or level (as of an atomic nucleus or a molecule) usually accompanied by loss or gain of a single quantum of energy

Preface

Have you ever noticed the topics of the conversations around you? At restaurants, in line at the bank, at the movies, in the mall or at the gym so often the subject turns to pets. And it is not just about how cute they are when they do this or that. It is just like talking about our kids. It is often about very specific accidents, diseases, and their sports skills (agility, flyball, swimming, Frisbee, etc.) and training. Our pets are in our thoughts all of the time. And, since we talk about what we think about, the subject turns to our dogs, cats, bunnies, birds, horses, etc.

I've noticed that dogs are the most often discussed. Cats are next. Their role in the family is different from that of dogs. They, and birds, rats, ferrets, fish, and other stay-at-home pets have more private relationships with their caregivers.

Dogs are out with their people, socially participating. They are our social lubricants, they offer a common ground for starting conversations with the strangers we see as our potential friends. We spend the time and effort in new learning curves to "socialize" them. We want to make sure that our dogs behave appropriately with people and other dogs.

They go everywhere with us. They're at the dog park, the forest preserve, walking around the city, playing with each other in back yards and driving around with their people in cars.

Pets are an outlet for us to express our deepest emotions. We can feel safe talking about our concerns, fears and interpretations of love with them. Many people are more comfortable talking about how much their pets influence their lives than how they are affected by other people.

Where it may not seem appropriate to discuss an ailing parent, it is perfectly okay, even fascinating to others, to discuss detail by detail, what happened at the vet's office that morning. Should something similar happen to their pet, a pet parent needs to know as much as they can, just in case.

We work through so much of our uncomfortable and unresolved grieving as we work on our relationships with our pets. The joys and pains of these intense, all too short-lived relationships help us develop beliefs about life and death. Pets provide us a venue to put the huge concepts of life and death into some sort of comfortable perspective.

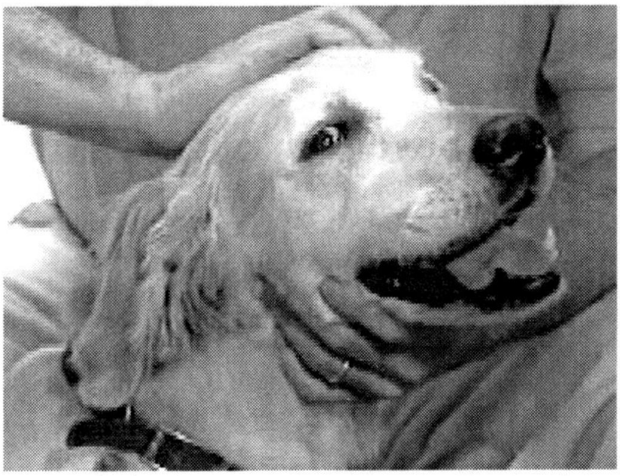

We use it as a format to think about the unthinkable. How do we handle the stress that comes with watching another suffer? What happens to us when we are helpless? How do we react when confronted by the natural law that says that we are all mortal; that life spans are finite?

Everything dies, we're told. We have difficulty really accepting death. It's an unknown. Nobody, we've heard, knows what death is or what it's like to die. It is hard to accept that someone we love will die; and that they could leave and abandon us. Death and dying are mysteries.

Some cultures teach that we ought to fear death. Some say that we should welcome it. Others profess that spirits hang around as advisors, companions or to be generally annoying. We're taught that there are places and experiences called Heaven and Hell. Some believe that when the physical body stops functioning, the spirit reconnects with a larger overall Master Spirit, or changes frequency and dimension, or merges back into a universal thought field.

What happens when we die, or when our beloved pets die? Your answer is uniquely your own. Your answer is based on your individualized version of what you have come to believe based on the stories you've been taught.

This book was written to help people who may be struggling to make sense of it all. It is a story of coming to terms and becoming comfortable with choosing the alternative of having a pet euthanized.

This book was also written to encourage animal massage and bodyworkers to incorporate Transitions PetMassage and grief therapy into their practice.

I would like to thank the veterinarians Paul Pifer, DVM and David Drake, DVM and staff at the Countryside Animal Hospital in Sylvania, Ohio for providing the experience of a death-time.

We students were ready.

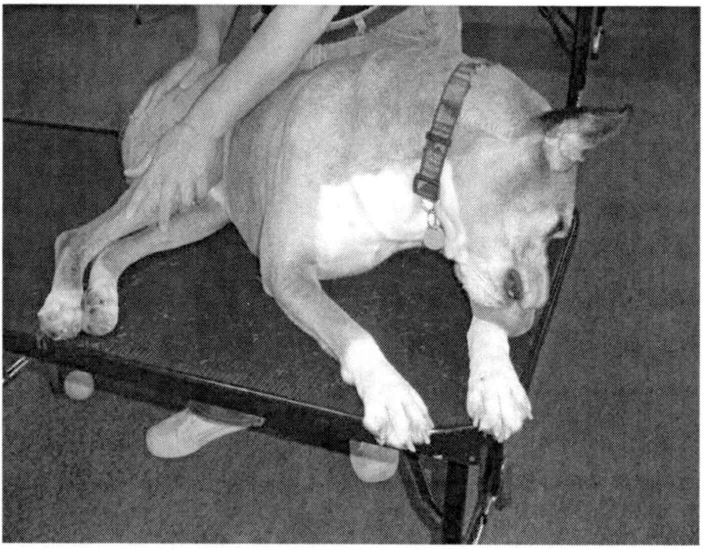

Oskar, Share the Dream, Gold Medal, Rudinger
May 1996 - January 2007

Oskar's story

Oskar always loved going for rides with us. Whenever he heard the door handle on the old Volvo click open, he would eagerly run up to the car, and as soon as the door opened he'd happily bound into his place on the back seat.

As we drove, Oskar would lean back against the soft leather back seat. He'd stare out the rear window, his head resting on the back ledge, watching whatever passed by.

After shopping, I would invariably return, to find him sitting in the driver's seat, looking like a formal chauffeur. His big boxer mug and brightly twinkling eyes drew attention everywhere we went. Strangers would smile and comment on how serious he appeared to be about his job as my driver. When I looked, he threw me his little ironic playful smirk.

We had a comic routine that we both enjoyed. He'd sit there in the front seat staring at me, questioning what I could possibly want him to do, all the while ignoring my exhortations for him to move. I would slowly lower myself onto what I considered to be my rightful place on the driver's seat. When he felt my weight moving into place, he'd scramble out of the way, back to his spot in back. Then, he'd simply turn his head to rest his chin again on the back of the seat.

Then, he started staying in the back seat of the car.

His rear legs grew weaker as he aged. I began to help him in and out of the car. He'd stand staring from the ground into the open car, anticipating his rear end being hoisted up so he could assume his position on the seat. His boost up became another cherished ritual for us.

His last few days were spent standing or lying in a sort of dazed state. No longer interested in going for rides, he was already starting his leaving process.

This photograph of him is with one of our other dogs and Anastasia at a forest preserve. That's Oskar in the rear. His life force was so diminished that he appears here to be fading into the winter brush. That's Lola, our new puppy in the foreground; alive and vibrant.

I'd carry Oskar outside for his bio breaks, after which, unsteady and disoriented, he'd remain standing, teetering, until I'd pick him up again. I'd carry him back inside and place him back in his favorite spot by the sofa where he could relax in the warm sunbeams patterning his body through the window.

His last day, Oskar appeared extremely uncomfortable. If he were touched he would startle, wince and quietly squeal. He had very little energy – his patience with his body, his stoicism, were virtually gone; as was his life force.

Oskar always had a creatively effective way of letting us know that he was upset. When he didn't like what was going on, he would trot around the room, leaving a wiggly trail of urine on the carpet. He told us in the most direct way possible that he was pissed off.

Sometimes after listening to emotional discussions or after the students and dogs had departed after the final day of a weeklong workshop, his trail would wind around the main classroom at the

PetMassage$_{TM}$ School; weaving in and out of the dozen PetMassage tables. His trail would continue through the offices and corridors. It was more about announcing his displeasure than marking his territory.

Oskar was a dog of few words. A dog of action. His favorite action was expressing himself in the international – interspecies – sign language of body language. His was a gentle soul and yet, a demonstrative one.

Concerned that his problem might be physical, we asked his vet to check him. He found him physically sound. And, the fact that the dog might have just emptied his bladder outside never seemed to matter, either.

Oskar was ... complex. He actualized the metaphor "pissed-off" to the letter.

If he weren't fed exactly at 5 PM he would let us know his opinion about it. If he were uncomfortable with any dogs or visitors that had just left our home or school, he would wait until they'd leave and show us the tide of emotions he had been holding back.

Whenever discussions around him became too loud or confrontational Oskar would let us know how uncomfortable he was with the emotional energy in the room. If anything around him interrupted the gentle flow of his internal Feng shui, he let us know he was pissed off.... by pissing off.

The evening before his final vet visit he was very weak. After his bio break (fluid in, fluid out), I sat with him on the carpet by his sofa in our living room. His PetMassage included the sequence for transition of the spirit. In the middle of the session, his eyes closed and he began to snore softly. He slept. I carefully eased myself away from him and silently, meditatively, left the room to get something to drink.

I returned to find him mustering his last tiny bit of energy. Oskar pulled himself up onto his wobbly legs.

And I watched as he scrawled his signature pee a-l-l a-r-o-u-n-d the border of our new oriental carpet. He then slowly returned, collapsing into his spot to accept the last rays of his afternoon sun.

The next morning he was so disoriented, he couldn't eat. He could barely stand. We called our veterinarian and made the arrangements. His euthanasia would be that afternoon. Then, as his condition deteriorated, we called again to reschedule his final appointment for within the hour.

I still had to shower and dress. So, I hurried up to shower on the second floor of our home. I turned on the water and stepped in. Then I heard a familiar sound. From the curtains I watched him as he slowly, unsteadily, stumbled his way up the 15 steps to the hallway landing and into the bathroom.

One of Oskar's favorite activities every morning had been sticking his big old boxer head into my shower and with closed eyes and ears flattened out to the sides in bliss; he'd lick the delicious soap off my calf.

Here he was, one last time. He poked his head into the spray, took a lick of Ivory, turned and stood unsteadily at the threshold of the bathroom door, staring into the hallway and gaping stairwell. His final act of comradeship was a valiant Herculean effort.

He told me what I needed to hear. He was ready. We were ready. I quickly dressed and carried him down the steps and out to the car. We both still had wet hair.

Oskar's euthanasia experience was quiet, peaceful and actually beautiful. Anastasia and I sat quietly with him in our veterinarian's exam room, petting him, concerned about how he was feeling, tracking our own feelings about what was going on, how we felt about choosing to have him "put down," and trying to come to terms with our own thoughts. We heard muffled conversations, incongruous with our reality, outside the door.

Someone was asking about breed standards and dog shows.

Oskar had come full circle.

He'd been a show dog too, in his puppyhood. "He could have been a contender," we heard from his breeders, trainers and handlers.

Oskar was given a sedative and within a couple of minutes, he sank down to the floor, fast asleep.

As he snored, we lifted him onto the exam table.

I stroked his head and shoulder, ribs and flank. With each of his heavy breaths, I felt his body expand and contract. I watched my hand rise and fall. It was surreal.

Oskar was given his lethal injection.

I rocked him and smoothed his coat as it took effect.

The body I rocked was his and then it was no longer him. It was suddenly strangely unfamiliar. An empty vessel, his life had quietly, spontaneously, slipped from his body and the room.

He was gone.

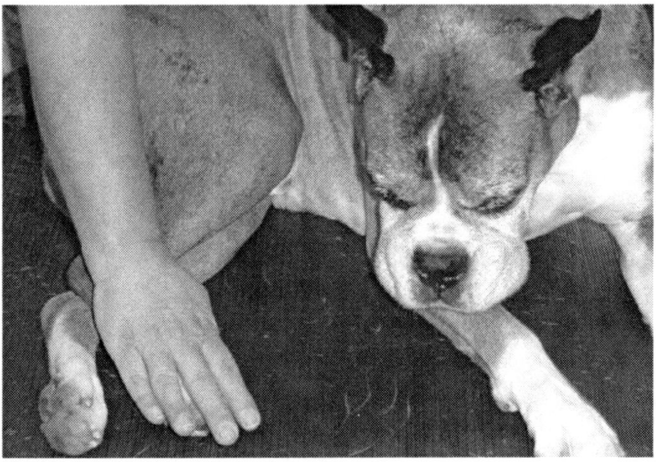

Oskar steps into
the labyrinth outside of time and space. One last memory: it was a good life; his waning presence smiles. Oskar's spirit returns to the universal ether.

His spirit, the most important part of him, the only part that mattered, was free.

He'd graced us with his years of his presence. His departure, was dignified.

He'd lived simply the law of nature. He abandoned the body that was no longer working for him. It was time to move on. We can miss him; and we cannot be sad for him.

He had always been a very cool dog. Now, physically, he was assuming room temperature.

He taught us about love and responsibility and the natural world. He taught us how to be responsible with dogs, with their people and with ourselves. He taught us to pay attention to our innermost feelings. It was always appropriate to express our truths, as we saw them. He made sure I learned my lessons with lots of hands-on repetition. I felt the need to pee. He'd done his job well.

Always a class act; he'd just taught us more lessons about grace and achievement through simply being. Now, Oskar was simply being gone.

Oskar's last PetMassage had been the previous evening.

Slow and uncomplicated, it was a mindful exercise in being present for each other.

Calmly and gently I had moved him through the sequence of energy vector connections and had methodically effleuraged his entire body.

He experienced his body through his responses to my touch, my compassion, my intention; my grace, one last time. I wanted him to relax. I wanted to let him feel the comfort of knowing that I loved him and honored him. He followed on the sincerity of my touch.

We connected on a profound level. Oskar and I shared a few special minutes of meditation and reverie. My intention was to help him. The process also helped me. The PetMassage was for both of us.

My objective was not to restrain him. I wanted to assist him – and me, to resolve any cross-connected memories that might resist the safe and easy release of our spirits.

He was to feel free to move on. So was I.

After the beginning of his PetMassage, we paused. We sat together on the carpet. In my reverie, I recalled random, inconsequential times we had shared. Oskar had a way of flattening his ears and tilting his head when he wanted affection.

He'd scavenge for apples under a tree outside our health club and usually bring one of them back into the car to snack on while we drove home. One time, through my rear view mirror, I noticed him sitting in the back of the car, hiding a golf ball in his closed grinning mouth, his head facing straight forward, his eyes rolling mischievously from side to side.

He'd get so excited whenever he was asked to jump onto a PetMassage table to be the demo-dog. One time during a class, while he was working, receiving a PetMassage, Jocko, our standard poodle dropped a chew-toy on the table in front of him. He stood still, like a good demo-dog and as he watched it out of the corner of his eye his body started to tremble. He practically exploded after the poodle, knocking the table onto its side.

And, he proudly, eagerly participated in his WaterWork PetMassages in our pool. As he was moved through the warm water, he'd let go of his tensions and his need to be in control. Flipped onto his back, floating, his body softened and drifted like seaweed. He'd learned to let go and just be ... wet.

I slowly progressed through the Transitions PetMassage sequence.

It was joyfully melancholy. We sat together. My hand resting on his ribs moved gently up and down with his breath.

Who knows what he was thinking? His breathing patterns and eye movements shifted from time to time. I'd like to think he was sharing a special moment.

I'd like to believe that it wasn't just gas.

We sat together in stillness on the carpet.

Photo: Cheryl Hall Photography

In our own ways we were both viscerally dealing with the situation. In my heart, I was feeling the nausea that tells me something is terribly out of balance.

His emotional response, as usual, would soon manifest from his bladder.

His grace is in our hearts and memories. It rests securely throughout our minds, bodies, and spirits; where everything is remembered and nothing forgotten.

It's also still in our carpet. He had clearly said his goodbyes.

Death
Nobody really understands death. Nobody understands life either, for that matter. As humans, we've been trying to make sense of what it means to be alive or be dead since we first became aware of ourselves. The unreality of death makes it an uncomfortable topic of conversation.

We've watched the seasons. Spring moves to summer, summer to fall and fall to winter. We've noticed a natural progression that apparently always ends in death; and still, we are not absolutely sure.

We've watched each other be born and give birth to more of us. We've grown and documented how we grow. Then, we've watched each other's bodies weaken in preparation for the progression of the evitable. Life and death are enigmas. They are mysteries within mysteries. We will never be sure; yet, we continue to strive to make sense of these phenomena.

One theory contends we return to the state that we were in before birth; pure potentiality. Perhaps it is going back to non-physical, pure energy and intention. Maybe it's some sort of limbo. Most likely, it is that we are delusional in our guesswork and it is entirely something else.

However we frame the questions and debate the possible alternatives, we do know one thing for sure. There is an essence of life force which moves away from its place somewhere within the body.

Where it goes, nobody knows.

Let's accept that there is a force in a living body that maintains the flow of energy through it. This life force maintains vitality, initiates growth, repair, and manages the aging process.

While this force is inhabiting the host body, there is growth and development. And, when it is not, the body experiences decay and atrophy. When it vacates the body after the host body for this life force is no longer serviceable, there is detectable movement of this something. This sounds like we are hosts for an extraterrestrial consciousness and that is exactly what it appears to be.

During an animal's lifetime, his experiences add to the

information already stored within his ET consciousness. The memories of newly acquired experiences are stored in the brain, the neurological system and in muscles and their connective tissue, the fascia. They are held in place within a web like matrix, supported and maintained through physical and emotional holding patterns.

Over 90% of memories are in the subconscious, the part of the mind-body complex, humming in the background. This is the software that makes living possible. These memories hold the massive wealth of background information that allows us to interpret, interact and survive. We could not maintain life without them.

This massive accumulation of our emotional connections with our dogs is there, in the fascia of their bodies. Sometimes at the time of their death, the emotional ties to their people are so strong, they can retard the natural dying process.

In Traditional Chinese Medicine, and now, in Western medicine, there is an acceptance of an essence of life force energy. It is called Ch'i. This Ch'i, Ki, or Qi (pronounced "chee") energy has a charge like electricity and magnetism.

It moves around the body via circuitry pathways called meridians. Ch'i can be measured and traced as it moves. If the movement is weak, the meridian is considered sluggish or stagnant. It can also be too strong, which would be a different kind of imbalance, it is considered excessive or overloaded.

Stagnant energy in or near a meridian disrupts smooth bodily activity and results in pain. *Qizhi* (pronounced "chee jee"), or *Stagnant Qi* is blocked energy usually experienced as a sharp pain.

An *excess* pattern appears when *Qi* energy pools at an acupoint, along a *meridian* or anywhere in the body where it becomes 'stuck.' It is often the first stage of disease. After *Qi* energy *stagnate*s, the *blood* will *congeal* unless energy is moved through the area.

What happens when someone dies? When the "stuff of life" has left, the body it leaves behind a hollow vessel. And this "stuff" of life: what happens to it?

In the body when all the activities of blood flow and respiration and consciousness have stopped, the Ch'i energy source that had been keeping everything going, has either gone dormant or, simply left.

Does it go somewhere else? Does it hang around the body-vessel for a time while it decides what to do and where to go next? Does it morph back into some sort of universal energy?

If it is connected to a greater source, as many of us have been taught to believe, does it operate within the same laws or are there different ones? Does it exist on different frequencies? Does it, can it, live within a different set of dimensions and in ways that we cannot fathom?

Does the spirit body have choices? Are there choices for it to make? Does it make choices? Is there an awareness within it that cares? When it no longer has access to the hardware of the mind and its nervous system with its physical memory storage systems, does it or can it have thoughts? Would they be thoughts as we understand them to be? Would they be based on the memories and information collected during its lifetime?

If it is in another dimension of consciousness, would it or could it still have independent, creative thoughts? Does it still acquire or require ego-based self determination? Does it have independence? Is there such a thing or a need for independence?

Our subconscious is the reservoir of all the impressions of our experiences and all of our memories starting in the stuff of star-dust and continuing to, well, now.

Is it possible that it belongs to a group of other life-stuffs? Perhaps these groups all share some common element or theme. Perhaps, not.

So many questions; so little time. When we offer PetMassage we can only be sure that we are assisting the life that we can see, before us. Whatever the answers, we would still like to see the animal's transition progress smoothly and easily from what we believe it to be happening now, to whatever is next.

The emotionally dependent ties that we have with our pets can indeed hold them -- and us -- back. Dogs, especially, are hardwired to want to please us. And if their natural process makes us unhappy, they will stoically hold on as long as they can, despite their own discomfort.

PetMassage$_{TM}$ transitions support is an effective tool when your dog is choosing to move from one life experience to another and/or to exit this life.

The Transitions PetMassage helps pet parent bodies find closure, too. Dogs and owners recall and recognize the sources and the patterns that may be inhibiting the normal, easy process. Often, remembering a traumatic experience and viewing it objectively, in an environment of safety and support, and with the added benefit of hindsight and maturity, reestablishes balance and clarity.

The Transitions PetMassage provides understanding, empathy and compassion. It helps to tie up the loose ends of unresolved relationships. It offers permission to move on. It provides openings where they are needed. It gives a supportive leg up when it is needed and requested.

PetMassage Transitions support has an important place in the animal massage profession.

We know that touch is necessary for emotional and physical survival. Without touch and attention, human infants and animals are underdeveloped. They are consistently weaker, smaller, more poorly socialized and less capable of expressing love, sharing and comfort. Without it human infants and animals show a failure to thrive.

Touch expresses compassion. Compassion, in the form of understanding, support and empathy works in concert with touch. The two cannot be separated.

The touch that is used in PetMassage$_{TM}$ has dramatic effects. It is a lot more than simply rubbing, stroking and squeezing the hair, skin and the connective tissue just under the skin. When we PetMassage a dog's body, the dog is universally transformed: body, mind and spirit.

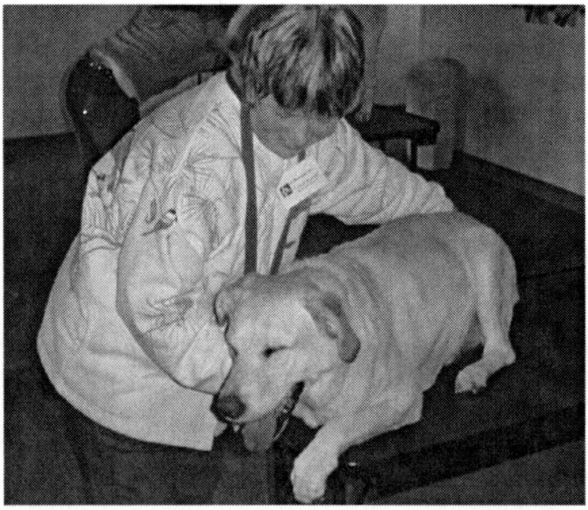

Change

Change is defined as a passage from one state, stage, subject, or place to another.

Another definition is "a movement, development, or evolution from one form, stage, or style to another, as, an abrupt change in energy state or level."

Change is a synonym for transition. Transition is defined as the passage from one state, stage, subject, or place to another.

The body experiences transitions throughout its life process. Some are major; some minor. The first big one is at conception, as it moves from the pre-evident, pure intention and potential to something that contains life energy.

Then there are all of the remarkable prenatal series of transformations to morph into a life from that we can recognize. At birth, life aquatic changes to life aerobic. Life confined to a tiny sack is opened to space and freedom. Learning to self ambulate, and express needs, wants and who they are through body language are the next big steps.

Each of us moves through each level of individualized growth and development. We live and experience life.

Each of us develops unique personalities that are ours alone. As we learn; we love.

Animals are no different than people. They often get stuck at significant transition points. The ones who cannot progress have "arrested development." The ones who can, evolve and grow.

Our perceptions of our life's experiences make us who we are. We have individual reasoning processes that we cultivate. Even the thoughts we have, the very premises for our reasoning, are the results of our perceptions of what we have experienced. We have internally integrated everything we have ever known.

We create the patterns in our lives. We choose how we move.

Each time you move from one thought to another, you are making a transition. As you read this, you are transitioning from one thought to the next. Points and periods of transition happen throughout our lives.

From a dog's point of view, there are the major ones like being conceived, moving through the phases of prenatal life, being born, detaching from his mother, discovering his social place of comfort in his little pack of puppies.

Then there is discovering what its like to be part of a human pack; navigating the ever changing circumstances of a new family, discovering what it feels like to have comfort and security.

Each skill adds to the mix of experiences that can be drawn on while developing skills for reconciling with other pets in the family, befriending the dogs next door, playing with the birds, squirrels and other wild neighborhood critters.

How he handles each of his learning experiences is based on the personality he brings into this life, and adds to the formulations for how he will live the rest of his life.

Everything that your dog experiences; everything he hears, sees, feels, smells, tastes, and reacts to is registered and stored in his subconscious memory. Every moment brings more minor events too. Everything.

Memories of how he felt in all of his experiences have indelibly marked their territories in his body, mind and spirit. He is perpetually assessing his immediate comfort level, safety, and group social relationships. Each is filtered through his memory of what he has experienced in his past. There is no dwelling on could haves, would haves or should haves. Your dog lives in a series of spontaneous awareness's and reactions. This is his nature.

In the best of times, your dog makes choices to live life to its full potential. He develops optimal health and wellness and inner body functioning. He maintains intuitive, unconscious, self-healing mechanisms. He practices intentional awareness. Your dog is a yogi.

If we allow ourselves to move naturally, flowing with our experiences, we, and our animal friends can live in present time.

Sometimes if the transitions have progressed less easily and smoothly, animals develop ways to protect themselves from perceived dangers.

They create behavioral (emotional) and physical patterns that they feel armor them against threatening situations.

These patterns are held in the body as iconic blueprints for reasoning, thoughts and perceptions. Like humans, all of their reasoning and reacting is an extension of these frequencies. These are holding patterns.

Holding patterns

A holding pattern is simply a habitual way of doing something. As with all skills, the first time you attempt to do something new, you are awkward and unsure in your movements and confidence. The next time is a little easier. The third time easier still. By the tenth time, it is already a habit. You are deliberately creating muscle memory. One example is learning to line dance. The first few times you feel clumsy and awkward, as your force your feet and body move in new patterns. Once you've "got it" with your feet, you comfortably start adding more skills, such as breathing, clapping your hands and smiling.

Have you ever learned to play a C chord on a guitar? Recall how you had to stretch your fingers of your left hand to press down on the strings just behind the frets with enough pressure so that when you strummed, the sound resembled more music than a muffled thrump. Within a few minutes, though, you no longer had to think about where your fingers were supposed to go. The muscles that controlled their movement had been retrained to move into the correct position, pressing with exactly the right amount of pressure.

Growing up extremely nearsighted, I had a hard time seeing things that were in the distance. When I half closed my eyes, and looked through the slit of light coming through my eyelashes, I could make out images that had been too fuzzy to see with eyes wide open. I still squint whenever I'm not understanding something. When I seek clarity, I return to a muscle memory pattern I had created to help me make sense of things I couldn't see.

When I was very young my parents would insist that I come along to visit my father's sister, who lived in Cleveland. Her enthusiastic greetings always included suffocating hugs and powerful Germanic pinching of my chubby little cheeks. Her greetings knocked the wind out of me and left sore, ruddy, pink marks on my face.

How I dreaded our visits to Cleveland where she lived. We would arrive at her home and I, having spent hours building up tension in my mind and body, would brace myself for the inevitable. My body stiffened and I held my breath as I endured her affection. As soon as it was over I could run off to play. She had her pattern. I had my pattern. We shared a pattern.

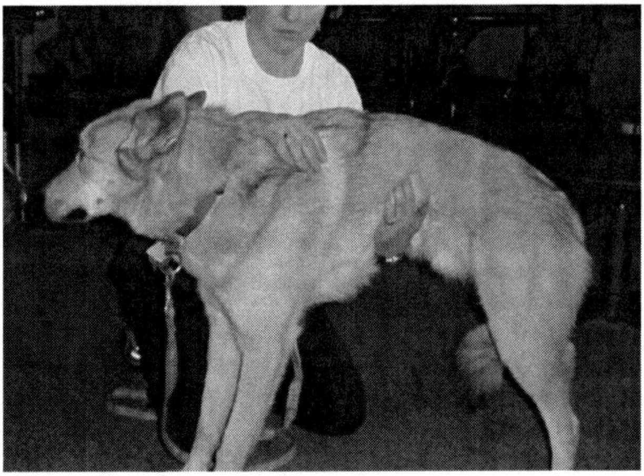

My daughter and her family have recently moved to Cleveland. These early memories of powerlessness and abuse are still mixed in with the other, more pleasant memories of birthday parties, playgrounds, and weddings. When I travel there to visit I take conflicting feelings of resistance and joy as carry-ons.

Stuckness happens. Emotional stuckness happens to all of us; especially our dogs. We get stuck in stultifying emotions like fear, guilt, remorse, selfishness. Dogs can get entrenched in habitual conditioned responses to sounds, smells, even shapes of people and specific movements that they make.

The first day that Oskar moved in with us, I made the innocent error of picking a newspaper up to throw it away. As I was rolling it up to shove it into the recycle can, he took one look at it and me and scrambled, cowering under the dining room table. I had inadvertently triggered a memory, an emotional holding pattern. Someone had either threatened him or "corrected" him with a rolled up newspaper.

If a dog is preoccupied and not paying attention to his immediate area and gets startled, he may hold onto that body space emotion. If another dog runs up and bites him on the butt when he's in that consciousness, he will feel vulnerable when anyone else approaches him from the rear. Dogs with fear aggression do not want anyone approaching them from the rear. The fear response gets triggered. The dog acts out.

Bringing a dog's body awareness to his rear end while he experiences the stimulus in a safe and comfortable environment, may help him overcome fear-based, habitualized responses.

We all have physical and emotional holding patterns. Some are healthy; some are not. We use them as guides to interpret what is going on around us and how we need to respond to what we've perceived. We've all been bitten in the butt, in one form or another. We all own and live from our rears (past). We do not have to live in the auto-response mode.

We have choices. We can free ourselves from convulsive, debilitating emotional loops and constricting thoughts. We can learn to pay attention to what we feel.

If we sense we lack the confidence to learn a new skill, or are unable to understand something, we all squint in our own ways. These are uncomfortable feelings. By becoming aware that we are feeling discomfort, we can choose to find a way to have a different experience. We can discover something or some way of acting, being, thinking, that will make us feel better.

It could be a treat reward, a pat on the head, the welcome sound of a clicker or a quick retreat to a safe distance. We have more choices when we are aware.

What do emotional stuckness, fear, discomfort and the potential to work through them have to do with PetMassage? This is where the memories of whether activities feel good or don't feel good come into play.

PetMassage is the intentional touch of an animal's physical body for the purpose of assisting him/her toward harmony and balance. PetMassage enhances awareness to every part of the body that it touches. In addition, through the convention of referral zones, myo-fascial connectivity, acupressure points and energetic channels of meridian pathways, the rest of the body that is not touched is also affected.

Each muscle cell in the body retains its own set of memories. Each of the memories relies on its experiences, or the perception of its experiences, of what was happening to it when it felt good and safe and what was happening when it didn't.

In addition to retaining experiences that happened in this lifetime, the cells hold all the long-term species' cultural-memories as cellular (or fascial) memory. This is the genetic information for the individual. Each little cell, then, shares in the responsibility for the well-being and the survival of the whole species. Each tiny cell is a hologram of the whole genetic line.

Every muscle cell maintains a perpetual relationship with the rest of the body

Traits, behaviors and personalities are stored and sourced in the genetic memories inherited from previous generations.

A Cavalier King Charles, for example, has a distinctly different point of reference and motivation for moving and interacting with his environment as compared to a Border Collie.

Pets often allow their current circumstances, as interpreted through their perceptions of safety and comfort, to overwhelm them. When a dog has a scary experience he'll recall a similar physical or emotional feeling and relive his initial fear response. Their perceptions could be based on real threats or imagined fears. Their reactions may become more neurotically extreme, the more they think about them. They *are* just like us!

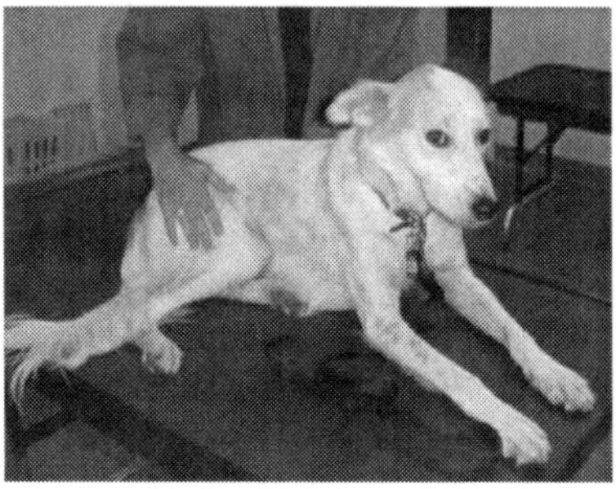

If your dog's body hurts when it's moved, he will figure out ways to move less or to move in ways that hurt less.

The unconscious way muscles are held in given emotional or physical situations to recover the place of comfort is a holding pattern.

Holding patterns are all unconscious. When a dog either notices the pattern, as I did with my squinting, or can identify some aspect of the source for it, such as seeing the relationship between being unable to see and understanding, he can make choices.

He can stay with the pattern or he can do something to reeducate his muscle memory. His body always has the natural tendency to move toward what he remembers as feeling secure and safe. Let's call this *moving to a place of comfort*.

In a PetMassage session we continuously request permission to be willingly allowed and accepted within the dog's personal space. PetMassage can only be effective with a dog's participation, guidance and cooperation.

This is easy for dogs. Their capacity for unconditional, nonjudgmental honesty is why we appreciate them so much. His role is to spontaneously reciprocate, honestly responding to whatever he feels or recalls. This is where they live. It's what they do.

The channels of communication between animal and human are continuous and profound. They are bridges for the sharing of energies, feelings and insights.

The simple act of observing, of being available, with the presence to witness them, has a subtle--and profound--effect on dogs' lives. It is unnecessary for you to be consciously aware of the specifics of your dog's internal dialog. Besides, that would be impossible. We don't even know what we are thinking most of the time. And when we do become aware, we wouldn't know how or where we got the information we base our assumptions on.

Choices for the unconscious, by, and of the unconscious happen on the deepest physical and emotional levels. We can never know which emotional tendril is being tweaked. It doesn't matter. Tweaking is being done. Whatever choices that are being made are only happening *because* of this particular relationship and stimulation.

Simply being present during the private sub-conversations going on within the tissues subtly helps in reeducating your dog's fascia memory matrix.

Within your body and touch, you are providing your dog with your pure presence. You are the support he needs to help his body naturally move back toward reestablishing its functional balance, homeostasis.

The super-intentionality of PetMassage reinforces your animal's internal decisions. Whenever his body experiences change, uncertainty, fear or pain, it armors itself. As part of the sympathetic nervous system's, fight or flight mechanism, muscles brace in flexion. Breath is held. Digestion stops. Self-restrictive postures, such as slinking, crouching, hunching and roaching reduce oxygenation, circulation, tissue hydration and overall flexibility.

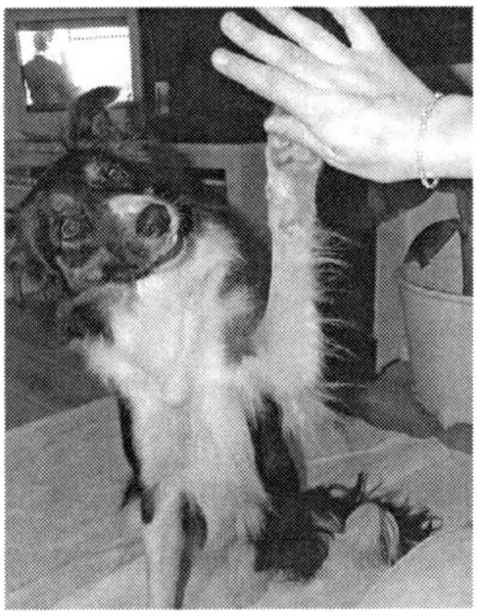

Holding patterns are not only physical. They are emotional and behavioral as well. Your dog has specifically developed thinking and reasoning patterns to make his life easier. His unique set of holding patterns underlies everything he does in his normal daily activities.

Holding patterns restrict or in some way influence all aspects of a dog's life. They determine the opportunities and choices he believes are available when he wants to move, behave and think in new and creative ways. Each new skill he learns, from raising his paw for a "high five" to remembering that you prefer him sitting next to the sofa rather than on it, requires continuing and consistent reeducation of physical and emotional holding patterns.

One posture dogs often develop is holding one leg up in the air like the little guy pictured here.

Your dog paws at your arm to get your attention when he needs to be taken outside to pee. He has found that this is a signal that you understand.

Your dog might have found that he is more comfortable when he sits on one hip, rather than on both haunches.

Hip discomfort is common in aging dogs. It challenged Oskar to discover ways to move his body that would support his quality of life. Experimenting with alternative postures, he kept doing what felt good and eliminated positions that were less comfortable. His body developed habitual ways to move and support its weight. He is resting on his left hip in the picture here. It was the posture he chose to adopt.

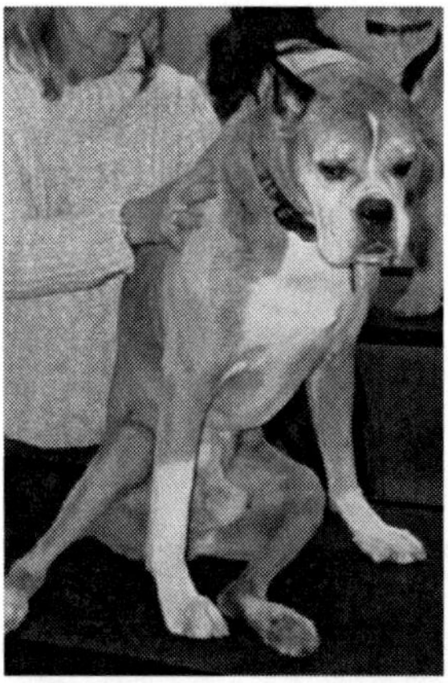

This posture may have assisted him in his release of built up gas. He had to have been assisted by something!

Posture affects the whole body. Habitual compensation for a sore hip creates a host of consequences: restrictions in oxygenation, dissymmetrical and uneven spinal, hip and shoulder muscle and ligamental development, reduced blood and neurological circulation, and a generally more sluggish system activity.

When leaning, the rest of Oskar's body had to be engaged to attempt to restore the body to a balanced state. Notice that Oskar's additional left foreleg weight bearing causes increased stress. Can you see how his neck bows to one side?
His head, balanced on top of the neck, cannot be held straight. Since Oskar's head is slightly tilted, his eyes cannot look directly or evenly forward.

Resting on one hip while sitting has other implications. In animal body language, this posture is a signal that projects weakness. It signals vulnerability. He is less formidable than if he were able to sit up straight. It says that he may be in pain; that he's too uncomfortable to maintain an upright, straight position. It says that he will be slower to act to defend himself. It says he might be irritable and cranky if approached.

This position also changes the chemistry of the dog's skin. We can only imagine how powerfully sensitive dogs are to scent. Following their instinctive chase reflexes, dogs notice and track anything that is moving away from calm, assertive balance. A dog in this posture will have soreness, inflammation, and atrophy of the muscles under his hip. Other dogs detect the odor of disease and degraded flesh.

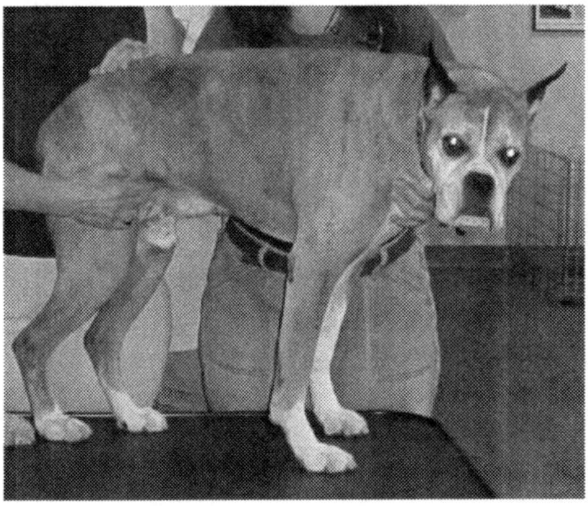

Over time as Oskar experienced the reactions of other dogs to his new set of postures, his emotional responses to them changed. He started acting old. He played less often with our other dog, Jacques, and when he did, it was with less vigor.

It would be fascinating to know what the initial trigger was for the discomfort.

Somewhere inside, secure in its mind-body-spirit complex, his trigger information was still there, along with all the other memories. The memories held within the muscles are supported and reinforced through movement and holding patterns. Oskar has Cleveland-style references, too.

Some patterns are short term. They are temporary adaptations to say, leg or hip tenderness after surgery or an accident. For a while, until the body heals, weight bearing is painful. The weight and the balance patterns shift, as the rest of the body compensates.

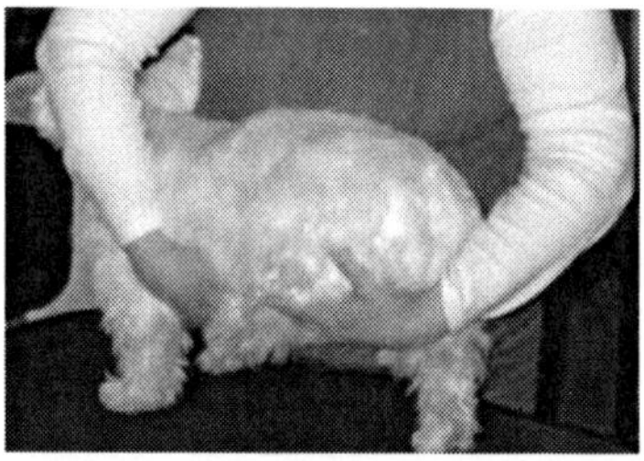

The temporary can become a habit with just a little bit of reinforcement.

Some patterns are learned. Consider our friend, Scooby, who while recovering from ACL surgery holds her paw up in discomfort. Her human rushes to her side with comforting hugs and treats. "What a great way to get goodies," Scooby reasons. "All I have to do is hold my paw up like this, and..."

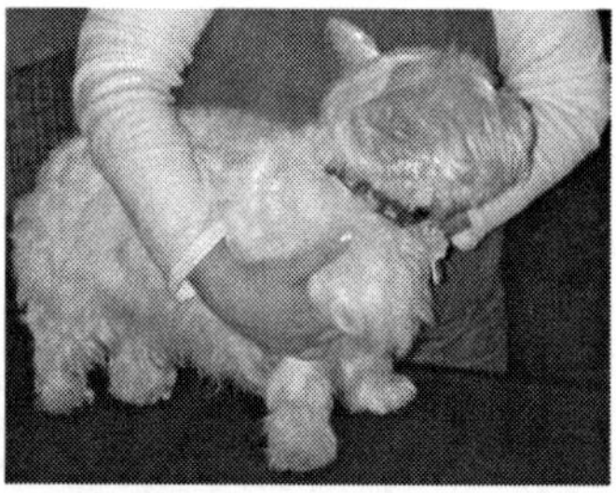

It's the beginning of another beautifully dysfunctional relationship. Scooby has a disincentive to resume weight bearing on that paw. And, now she has a very good reason to allow her body, and overall health, to deteriorate.

Soon, her body develops ways to habitually compensate. Scooby's musculature becomes contorted. The spine is pulled into misalignment, restricting breathing and compressing the organs so they cannot function efficiently. Her immune system, overworked and underpaid, goes on strike. Muscles, tendons, ligaments and bones that had been used to walk and bear weight start to waste away.

The Scooby, as we knew her, is lost. She's in and out of rehab. Drugs, alcohol, tattoos and piercings become her passions. The Scoob-ster could end up on the street, accepting non-organic treats in tough neighborhoods. It's a sad spiral; all because her human comforted her with the wrong signals. What's a Scooby to do?

An acquired holding pattern like Scooby's can be observed, supported, and released with PetMassage. Holding the limb in a slightly variant position with specific pressures and movements encourages the dog to remember, for himself, which positions create a sensation of safety and comfort and which won't.

PetMassage rekindles and reeducates the memories in muscles, myo, and the layers of fascia, that hold them in place. This is myo-fascia massage work. Through myo-fascia PetMassage dogs are given opportunities to choose to become more balanced, energetically.

The whole body, inside the skin, on the surface and in the spaces around it, is a complex network of dynamic pressures and pleasures.

The body-mind's newly created patterns and decisions; now *intentions,* open your dog to healthier, possibilities and options.

Everywhere, the body experiences looseness and tightness, freedom and constriction, balance and imbalance, harmony and disharmony. All the feelings and memories of emotions associated with these conditions are imbedded in ours, and our dogs', psyche-fascia. Fear is a component of a memory. Joy is another. We know our worlds the way we do because of the emotions we felt with experiences.

The sounds of doors slamming, angry voices, and images of newspapers being rolled up all trigger the emotional memories.

The hinge of the pantry door creaks as it opens. A bag of kibble rustles quietly when it's touched. It has a frequency that reverberates through the house. There's food in that bag! These are spontaneous recollections of the feelings of similar experiences. These are emotional responses.

There are emotional responses attached to all memories. The sound of your voice, a key turning in the lock, the sound of your car in the driveway, squirrels, the aroma of food being prepared, the scent of your clothes, your shoes, your favorite chair, other squirrels, your vet's office parking lot, your groomer's nail clippers, and the smells of, well, just about everything.

Patterns are naturally and automatically created in the quest to live in a more comfortable body; in a safe, secure, more comfortable space. They are drawn from your dog's private trove of experiences. They are all reinforced and held fast, in muscular movement and behavioral patterns, based on thoughts and feelings.

Fascia
Your dog's memories of the emotional responses to these experiences are retained in his/her muscles and fascia. Fascia is the matrix that forms and maintains muscles, skin, and much of the connective tissues in the body.

From the perspective of PetMassage$_{TM}$ bodywork, this is how the body works.

Each tiny muscle fibril is encased in a thin casing (like the skin on a hot dog) of connective tissue that allows the muscle cells within it to work in unison, contracting or expanding together. The casing is called fascia. Millions of muscle fibrils combine to make a muscle fiber, which is also encased in a thin fascia sheath so that its contents can work in unison. Millions of muscle fibers create a muscle, encased in fascia. Several muscles, working together, create muscle groups. You guessed it; they too, are encased in fascia. Deltoid muscles, hamstrings and masseter muscles are just a few of the examples that come to mind.

Every fascia-encased group of skeletal muscles spans across one or more joints.

The fascia sheathes around the muscles, are less elastic and stronger than the expanding and contracting muscle tissue. Sheathes of fascia come together to form the ends of muscles that connect muscles to bones; they are the tendons.

The proximal, closer to the midline of the body, ends of the tendons attached to bones are known as origin points. Muscle tendon distal attachment sites, ones that are further from the midline, are called insertions. When a muscle group contracts, it creates movement by shortening the muscles, pulling the insertion end toward the origin. Flexing/shortening, changes the angles of the bones at the joint. When the muscle group relaxes, the muscles lengthen, and the distal end of bone is allowed to move away from the midline of the body.

No muscle is an island. Muscles have to work in unison with each other. The agonists are the muscles that cause specific movement or possibly several movements to occur through the process of their own contraction; another group controls the amount of agonist flexion with the opposite behavior, extension. They are the antagonists. Other muscles support the movement although they are not directly involved in it. They are the synergistic muscles.

Muscle groups need to coordinate their activities with each other, such as all of the muscles around the head, in the neck and around the shoulder. The combined groups are contained in sheathes of, what was that term? Oh yes, fascia.

The separate groups overlay each other, slipping and sliding over one another during movement. The larger groups of fascia all coordinate their movements with adjacent bundles of fascia, too. When one area of your dog's body is held in a fixed, protective manner, it affects the movements of muscles and fat and blood circulation contained in adjacent fascia.

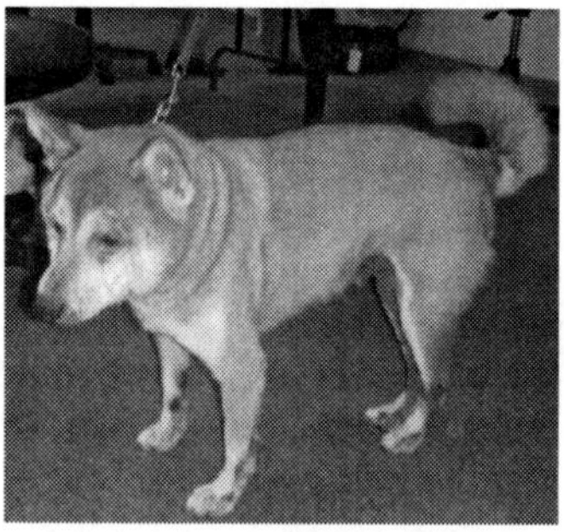

For example, when the tissues around a dog's eyes are swollen, the excess fluid stretches all the fascia of all the muscle groups on the top of the skull. It contorts the bundles of muscles on that side of the body controlling the ears, the mouth, the neck, shoulders and foreleg. The muscles on the opposite side are also affected. They have to compensate for any variations from normal body patterns.

When a toenail on one of the forepaws gets torn and causes pain, an animal will alter his gait so that his paw doesn't have to support as much weight. What happens if he turns his foot in and discovers he is slightly more comfortable in this new position?

As his elbow is thrust out to the side, the entire foot and lower leg becomes skewed. The fascia containing the muscles, fat, blood supply and nerves of his upper arm and shoulder twists, opening the scapula, stressing the shoulder capsule and all the attendant structures attached to the shoulder blade. Continuing, the platysma muscles and fascia in the neck are drawn back distorting the side of the face. His torn nail is directly connected to increasing pressure on the sinuses around his eyes and his cranial muscles.

Other muscles attached to the shoulder blade, the scapula, impact the movement of the ribs, affecting his capacity for breathing.

Shallow breathing changes the pressures in the abdomen which affects peristalsis and digestion. Imagine; all from a sore toenail!

This is where it really gets even more interesting. There was a reason for this section on anatomy and physiology. Thank you for your patience. It really does all come together.

Fascia, we've seen, in one part of the body, affects the quality of movement of the entire body.

Fascia, in one part of the body, affects the quality of life of the entire dog.

Fascia in one part of the body, affects the quality of life of the dog's entire pack, including his human family.

Your dog's body, when it is in balance in the way it functions, maintains health, structural integrity and peace of mind. It glows with body-mind-spirit comfort and harmony.

We've seen that discomfort creates spasms, guarding, and tightness. The body intuitively seeks ways to protect and compensate for itself through its intricate network of fascia relationships.

Discomfort and its extenuating effects on the rest of the body also cause frustration, anger, and a host of other emotions. It works on all levels. It is an essential part of the mind - body - spirit, connection.

When the body is out of balance, its life force energy, Ch'i, is dimmed. Remember though, its normal tendency is to be always seeking balance, wholeness, wellness and homeostasis.

We've seen that fascia affects and is affected by, the whole body. The whole body is not limited to just the physical meat; it also includes the space immediately around it. The entire body is encased in external fascia; layers of energy shells.

Energy shells, the aura, are spontaneous extensions of whatever is going on in the body, emotionally or physically. These are pure, nearly physical, extensions of thoughts and fears, dreams and wishes. Absolutely honest, they are expressions of who the animal truly is and what he feels in the real world of universal nature. They show as, and feel like, spikes of energy radiating, spinning, from the body.

The aura can be as big as a room; filling it with joy, exuberance and awareness. It sparkles as it reflects health and happiness, confidence and well-being.

It can also be held tightly close to the body. Compact and dense, it is enough to enable the body to feel as if it were protected within a coat of thick armor. This aura feels dark and full of dread when it reflects disharmony, sadness, fear, a sense of being ignored and unappreciated.

Auras can be loose and open. They can be tight and closed. They reflect what is happening to the life in the body. Energy shells can be in balance or out of balance.

Auras, the energy patterns in the fascia surrounding your dog's body, are reflections of how the inner body systems are doing and how he is coping with them.

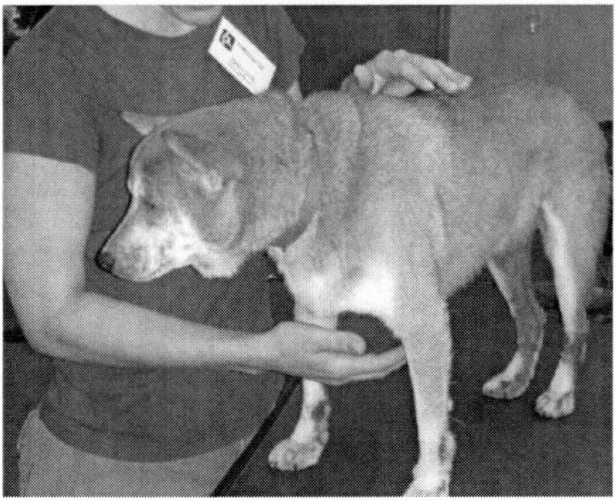

Fascia auras are a route back to the body.

PetMassage techniques influence your dog's external, auric fascia. Affecting the external, auric fascia affects subtle changes within your dog's body.

Any tiny variations can have a huge long term effect. Think of how the slightest change of an airplane's course, at the beginning of a flight, changes its path, destination, length of time in the air, and even volume of fuel used.

PetMassage external fascia work supports tiny life course corrections which alter your dog's body's entire range of activities. Your dog's willingness and ability to function is enhanced.

External fascia work supports and facilitates the transition process from this plane of existence to whatever's next.

The final transition (we observe) is death.

The Transitions PetMassage: assisting transitions
There is an invisible force field around everyone's body. Envision it as an auric body space. It is the first line of defense for the body and mind. It protects the spirit.

The aura, or energy body, is not solid. It is a pattern of thought forms. Its frequencies and densities move and change as easily as thought and feeling slip and slip throughout unconsciousness.

They reflect a person's, or an animal's, or a plant's, life condition. If your dog is feeling great, his field will be strong and vital. If he is feeling weak and vulnerable, his field will project an energy that is weak and vulnerable.

The body wants to protect itself when it becomes aware that it is in a weakened and vulnerable position. It will naturally work to create a private refuge where it can hide to lick its wounds. The energy barrier functions as a body cave. Energetic armoring protects like a turtle's shell.

The aura body is the energetic personal space that each of us live in. These thought-forms functionally protect us. They connect and communicate with other thought forms. The aura body is an important sensing tool that we use intuitively to protect body-space.

All of us animals and plants have finely tuned internal mechanisms to assess our safety in our surroundings and to read each other. Flowers contract their petals and turn their leaves to the side. Animals in the wild pay close conscious attention to it. It is also a mechanism that is, as we shall see, present – and operative, around the body while it is dying.

The dogs pictured here know how close they need to be to each other for everyone to be comfortable. Each one projects his own amount of personal space. Notice that they appear to be aware of each other's boundaries.

Our intuitive bodies pay attention even if our conscious minds don't. Within our reservoirs of unconscious, historical awareness, we have total recall of the emotional memories, experiences and lessons of thousands of generations.

When the body field senses a stressor the "fight or flee" response is activated. It changes our lives, or, changes the priorities of the way the body functions. The respiratory rate increases. Blood is shunted away from the digestive tract and directed into fast-twitch muscles, which require extra energy and fuel for running and fighting. Pupils dilate. Awareness of surroundings intensifies. Eyesight sharpens. Reactions quicken. Even, the perception of pain diminishes.

How connected we and our dogs are to our species memory! This intuitive awareness is just one use of the energy fields we hold around us.

Energy fields have characteristics such as thickness, thinness, transparency, opacity. They have density, texture, and detectable temperature variations. Many people have developed the skills to perceive the shapes, colors, and frequencies of energy fields.

Medical intuitives interpret the patterns they "see" in the energy field. The patterns can derive from this lifetime's events or memories from previous experiences. If you are not convinced about the veracity of past life memories, just think about the information stored in the DNA and RNA. What would have been the sources for intuitive memory responses such as the fight-or-flight or chase response?

Energy fields have layers. The superficial or outer levels express currently held thoughts, moods, relationships and health conditions. One major influence is spontaneous thought.

You are walking around outside, enjoying the sunshine, the beautiful trees, the birds chittering in the distance. You are humming to yourself and feeling great. Then you stub your toe. Every part of your energy shifts and screams. You see red, your body tenses and you catch your breath. Your thoughts are no longer on serenity; they are all about your sore toe. You wonder if anyone saw you trip. And, if they did, do they think you are clumsy. Your energetic body spontaneously contracted to protect your toe and your self image.

More entrenched beliefs are held deeper. The thought forms held close to the body are extensions of chronic (thought, mood, relationship and health) conditions.
They are prominent, like a bandage or dressing over areas that need protection.

Deeper and denser, still, are the species cellular memories. Your DNA and RNA are receptacles and administrators of much of this information.

The energy field responds to certain frequencies, such as sound, light, color, aroma, flower essence, air quality and movement, and prayer. It also is affected by its position in a room in relation to other thought-forms and inert objects around it.

Every cell in the body responds readily, as do all life forms, to touch. The conscious, the subconscious, the unconscious and the super conscious layers all rise up to meet, greet and network with PetMassage$_{TM}$ intentional touch. This is a way for you to access your dog's immortal inner puppy.

We've described the palpable and perceivable attributes of the energy fields. They also incorporate highly responsive tracts of information about energy flow that move along the meridian lines of Traditional Chinese Medicine.

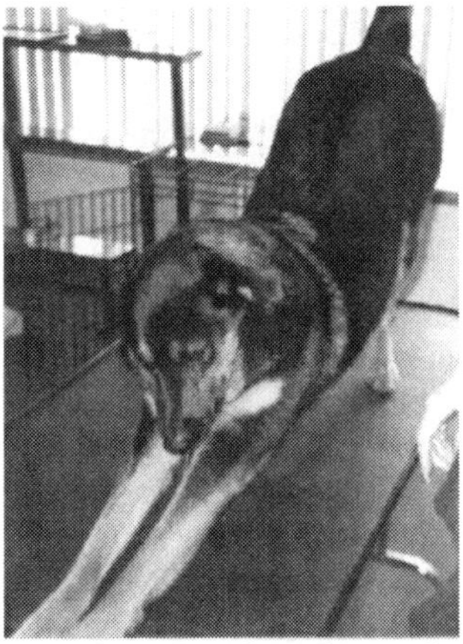

The two that we will discuss here are the routes that follow the channels of two major meridian lines, the Ultimate Yang: Governing Vessel and the Ultimate Yin: Conception Vessel. The Conception Vessel pathway runs up the ventral (underneath) midline of the body from the under the tail to the chin.

The other meridian, the Governing Vessel, runs up the dorsal (topline) of the body along the midline, from the tip of the tail, over the spine, the top of the head and muzzle to the middle of the upper lip under the nose.

These pathways, or seams, are within the fabric of the body field. These energetic seams can be strong and vital, or they can be weak, tired, worn, soft, and/or permeable.

Visualize zippers running through these two seams. A closed zipper can be opened and an opened one, closed. To unzip, opens the seam. Zipping up, closes it.

Unzipping moves in the direction from the head, down toward the tail, over the topline and, on the ventral (belly) side, from the chin to the anus. To zip back up, follow the opposite direction, moving over the topline, from the tail toward the nose, and on the bottom line from the tail, across the belly, chest, and neck, to the *philtrum*, the little divot on the upper lip, beneath the nose.

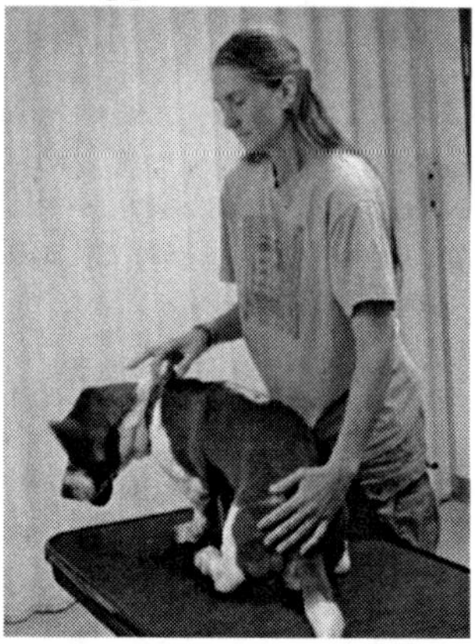

Your hand position is the same as if you were pulling up a zipper on a jacket. Rest your thumb against the side of your middle finger and trace the line of the seam with your fingernails.

Using the zipper will help you access your dog's inner puppy to assist him through each of his life and lifestyle transformations.

If you sense you are having difficulty connecting with a dog you are working with and notice that you are working in his energetic armoring, there are some things you can do. First notice the source of the resistance. Is it you or the dog?

If you are apprehensive around dogs with black tongues, you project that emotion. You cannot hide it. If you are concerned when working with larger, more aggressive dogs, you may, whenever you work with a Shepherd, a Rottweiler or an Akita, project fear.

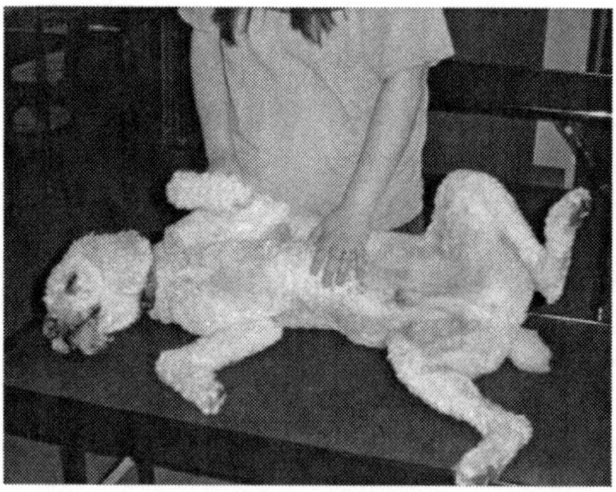

Your connection with each dog is biased; based on experiences with similar dogs or similar situations. You may have a tendency, when you sense that there might be resistance to your overtures, to want to meet it with a similar energy. Your intention to overcome or overpower your perception of resistance could inadvertently escalate an already stressed situation.

Nobody is comfortable with every breed of dog. I admit it. I have a preference for Boxers. There is just something about the goofy boxer exuberance that makes me smile. And dobies ... oh, and weimaraners and shepherds and standard poodles, bulldogs, pits, and giant dogs and some laid back small ones. I'm not a terrier person, and border collies and Aussies are just too intense for my comfort. It is normal, and okay, to have preferences.

So, if the resistance is coming from you, regroup and quiet yourself. Your observation of your thoughts can significantly change your aura ... and your dog's receptivity to your touch. Observe your breathing. Reestablish in your mind that you are safe and secure. Change your perspective and your thought-form relationship with your dog. Shift your weight to your other foot. When you've regained your composure, reconnect with him. The dog in your hands is forgiving and more aware of your energy than you are. He will synchronize his mood with yours.

If it's not coming from you, resistance could be coming from the dog in your hands, who may be frightened, acting out, or yielding to old hooks to emotional holding patterns. You'll recognize spinning, growling, and backing up or cowering, when you see them. If it is the dog's stuff, again, make sure you feel safe in his presence. Offer your quiet controlled presence as an oasis of calm in the chaos of his worldview.

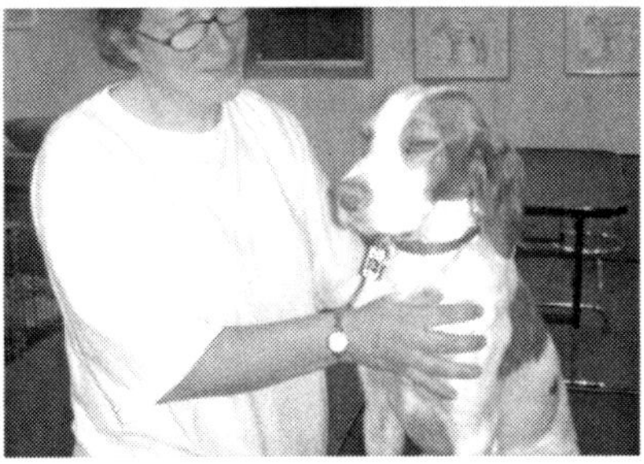

Again, observe your breathing to regroup and quiet yourself. Reestablish in your mind that you are safe and secure. He will soon come to you for support.

Never force your intentions on an unwilling dog.

After asking and receiving his permission to enter his space, quickly unzip his energetic armoring. You have only a momentary opening to access his Shen, spirit. Move your hand cranial to caudal, from the head to the tail, slicing your thumb and middle fingertips through his energy field, over the sagittal midline of the body.

Quickly move into his space and begin the vector sequence (see pages 60, 76-77). Notice how much more open and receptive your dog has become.

Armoring can be so tight and restrictive that on the first pass you may not be able to comfortably access his physical body. In this case, you may have to begin with vectoring four to six inches away from his body. Hold your hands at this distance until you feel the resisting field around his body soften. As it does, your hands will be permitted to move in closer to his body.

Observe your dog's reactions. Note his body language: ears, eyes, tail and mouth. What is his body telling you? Is he shaking? Trembling or still? Is his nose down or up? Is he cowering or on his back? Has his respiration changed? Is he panting heavily or does he exhibit especially sweaty paws? If his normally pink tongue turns dark or gray, it indicates he is stressed, dehydrated and lacking in oxygenation.

Once your dog is comfortable with your presence and you are in, continue your basic, full body PetMassage.

Continue to assess his reactions to you and continue to keep asking for permission to stay there with him. It is the dog's PetMassage. It is for his benefit. He has the option and right to change his mind at any time.

When your session is complete, remember to zip his body back up. Left open, it may leave him feeling vulnerable. We can all relate to that awkward feeling of embarrassment when we discover our zipper is open!

If you do forget, it will not harm your dog. He will intuitively, and spontaneously, figure out a way to close his protective cover.

In martial arts, the body is made vulnerable to attack by "unzipping" it with the motion of quickly swiping your hand down through the aura from the head to the navel. When I was in college, I used this technique with great success in fencing class to create openings for the touché.

There is another way to reseal the field. The first, you recall is to zip it back up, moving your hand upward from caudal to cranial. The other is to move it across, in a side-to-side motion, over the area of the heart.

As a religious rite, the gesture of crossing one's chest with the vertical movement of the hand symbolically and energetically opens your chest and heart. It opens the gates of your body-mind and spirit to accept serious spiritual power. The side-to-side gesture seals the deal. "Cross my heart and hope to die," completes the acceptance contract.

Opening the zipper is a way for you to assist your dog when he is transitioning from any of his phases to the next: puppy to adolescent, young to old, life to death.

Incorporate zippering into your PetMassage.

Begin by calming yourself by controlling and observing your breathing. Ground yourself. Feel yourself rooted through the floor so that you can channel whatever you sense of earth energy to flow in support of your dog's life force.

Engage your dog's energy patterns and reinforce them with vectoring connections. Vectoring is holding the specifically ordered PetMassage series of double points on the dog's body and visualizing/witnessing the flow of energy from the center of one of your palms, through the tissues, to the center of the other palm.

Why vector? The job of a dog is to watch, and to be vigilant. He protects his space and yours. Ever on guard, he is encoded, or emotionally needing to be outwardly focused. His job gives him purpose and satisfaction.

Vectoring increases your dog's body self-awareness. It redirects his attention from external to internal, from without his body, to within.

As he follows the movements of your hands on his body, his attention is drawn in. Slowly and mindfully enhance your dog's total body awareness with the full series of assessment strokes on his body. Intention follows attention.

With your dog's permission unzip the auric body, sluicing your fingertips through the auric body field from nose to tail, cranial to caudal. You can work either on the dorsal, the topline, or the ventral, the underside, or both.

Use both hands to gently comb through the aura. Spread the separate layers of the shells laterally from the midline toward the sides'. Repeat this motion 2 or 3 times.

Visualize the field open and splayed.

You may feel the need to move further away from the body with each pass. Each distance you work in is its distinct energy shell. Follow your intuition. Whatever you feel, you are right. At this point, as long as you stay open and present, your hands will be guided by your dog.

This sequence removes restrictions and creates an environment for alternative inner reeducation. It encourages the movement of your dog's pure spirit from his body's core, to the surface and out, to play with the softer, more fluid energies.

If this is part of an end of life Transition PetMassage, do not rezip your dog's aura. Allow it to retain this open position. There is also, no need to ritually ground the dog after the PetMassage. We want to encourage him/her to follow-on with the natural progression of end of life releases. If he needs to reconnect, just as if you had forgotten to close, he will recover himself.

The effects of the Transitions PetMassage are not always immediate. Each dog's life and experience is unique. Some dogs make their transition quickly, spontaneously or within a few hours. Some take several days. Some use the session to reevaluate and decide the path that they are already on is the one for them. Some use the session to rebound to better health.

Trying to anticipate how your dog will respond will soon teach you not to get too attached to an expected outcome. This is a lesson that is sometimes hard to accept. Remember that it is the dog's PetMassage, his life, and his choices.

Sometimes, the guardian or the one who is the facilitator may be the one who gains the needed spiritual relief.

As you might recall, with Oskar, the unzipping did, in fact, open his body to release his spirit. It provided relief, release and permission to move on. It prepared Oskar. It prepared me. It enabled both of us to be ready for the euthanasia experience.

If your dog is not ready, your treatment will not induce death.

It will not bring dark thoughts of impending doom into your dog's brain. You are not calling on any weird spirits. You are merely working with the facilities that are already there; albeit, now, in a more knowledgeable and direct way.

Even if these procedures are not followed perfectly, they will not and cannot harm your dog. They can only facilitate. They are tools for you to use to support the natural progression from one life phase to whatever's next.

Working with the natural properties of animals is hardly a new concept. These practices have been around and provided by medicine men and women all over the world for tens of thousands of years.

End of life care and assistance
Animals are usually happy go lucky as they play and eat, sleep and work, day to day. Like world class athletes, no matter how well they feel, no matter how well their bodies are functioning, they can always be more efficient in their moving and shaking.

PetMassage is a process that affects the animal's entire body, mind and spirit experience. Envision a scenario in which all of your pet's natural tendencies toward wholeness and homeostasis are optimized. All systems are "Go". Everything works better. Everything feels better.

PetMassage helps animals connect with, develop and maintain ambient inner environments. Food is in an environment where it can be processed efficiently. Eyes are clear and attentive. Ears are perked in awareness. The coat is glowing. Teeth and nails are strong. Your pet easily and comfortably runs and jumps. Even play is more fun.

When sleep comes, it is more profound, using the dream encounters in the shut-eyed, leg-thumping horizontal otherworld to work through and heal emotional confusions.

We've seen how, throughout the life of an animal, PetMassage assists in the natural release of physical and emotional stress. PetMassage enhances the quality of life at every stage. PetMassage can make every movement and every moment easier.

The end of an animal's life is an important and essential part of his/her existence. It needs to be treated with the same respect, support, understanding and love as was given the rest of their life.

Torpor is released, allowing the spiritual essences of life to soar for freedom.

The love you share with each other is unconditional.

The emotional and spiritual redirecting that the animal massage-bodyworker provides for both pet and pet parent are especially significant at the final transition.

Animal massage and bodywork helps you, the pet parent, understand and accept the naturalness of the grief that you feel. The surviving members of the pet's family all benefit from the acknowledgement that his death is a natural part of the

progression of life. It is an important part of being open to connecting to your dog and assisting in his process.

Everyone processes the grief they experience in his/her own way.

What does it mean to grieve? An *Encarta* definition describes grieving as having "the experience of great sadness, for example, at a death or a loss."

It is a response to loss that is organically real. It is uncontrived, and uncontrollable. Originating somewhere deep within the core of the body-mind and spirit. It is not a response that we can choose or decide to experience.

At times of loss, we do feel sad; sad and empty. Sometimes it comes on so hard and fast that it kicks in the stomach and knocks the wind out of you. Just being able to take that next breath can be a major accomplishment.

Sometimes we don't appear to feel anything; our emotions do not appear to be working as we think they ought to.

It is not uncommon for people to feel guilty because they are not as sad as they think they are supposed to be. Not to worry. The sadness is there. It is just waiting for a more opportune time to express itself.

There are many reasons to grieve. We grieve the loss of anything we've lost, especially the feeling of being in control. When anything in our lives changes, we miss the sameness that we had before. When we move to another home, we miss the comfort of knowing where everything is; the grocer, the library, the coffee shop. In a relationship change, you may miss the interactions, the routine, and the ease of being with someone familiar.

We can have regrets. We've all missed opportunities at brass rings that would surely have changed our lives and provided everything we could ever wish for. Nice rings.

Not all losses are devastating; and some are. The loss of a beloved pet can be gut wrenching.

How does one cope when their life has been suddenly turned inside out? Where can you turn when your support, your best friend, the one you have been depending on as an outlet for your affection, is on his way out or is gone? Who will be there to keep you company?

Right here, right now, you need to know that the intensity of the sad feelings you may be experiencing will diminish. It always does. You will never forget your animal friend. With time and moving through the various stages of grief, you will be ready to enjoy another quality relationship, not the same one, but one as strong, with another dog or cat or horse or iguana or chicken or ---- .

Some losses do not have an apparent immediate intense impact. My mother's parents died several years apart. She saw herself as the tower of strength whose function was to be the support for her family. My mother did not cry at either of her parents funerals.

My mother and her brother were very close. When he died, she did not cry.

My parents ran their own business for many years. During a regional economic recession in the early 1960's, they experienced severe financial troubles. It affected their lives in so many ways: loss of income, loss of self regard, and loss of confidence. My father's health declined and he sank into a deep depression. My mother was, once more, the tower of strength. She didn't cry.

Then one day our family dog, Pepper, after a long and delightful life, died. My mother threw herself on the bed and sobbed for days.

Pepper's passing was the trigger that allowed her to release a lifetime of pent up grief and sadness that had been stifled and smoldering deep inside her.

After her crying was complete, she still felt sad. She still missed Pepper. Yet she felt somehow lighter, cleansed. She had been emotionally and spiritually freed. Without restraining the experience, without consciously deciding that it was time to pop the lid on her internal controlling pressure cooker, she was able to begin to process and progress through the natural stages of grief. She was able to begin the healing for all her other losses.

Unresolved emotional resentments and hurts are dangerous. They gnaw away at a person's or an animal's insides until they create real physical irritation and disease. One theory suggests that the original causation of *every* disease is emotional stress. In my mother's situation, her unconscious pent up and unresolved, emotions were stressors. Her grief, unresolved, gnawed away at her psyche and her insides for much of her lifetime. It could easily have been the progenitor of the cancers she battled during much of her life.

Our pets have shorter life spans than we do. Many people do not have a dog now because they would not want to go through the experience again of having to deal with the loss of a best friend. It can be devastating.

Death does not have to be sad. It does not have to represent a loss. For Anastasia, my wife, and me, when we assisted in the euthanasia of our wonderful 10 ½ year old boxer, Oskar, it was a natural, beautiful experience in which everyone won and we all gained.

In our PetMassage practice we have the opportunity to help not only the transitioning dog; we can help his/her survivors, his human pet parents, and fellow pets. Our support helps these loving guardians of animals release their anxieties and feel some relief.

Through understanding and the process of witnessing, simply staying within the presence of the guardian, listening and reassuring, we have the opportunity to relax and nurture them.

People often get swept up in the emotional whirlpools of their circumstances. Sometimes when a pet is in the last stages of life, it feels overwhelming. We need a support system more than ever.

In the final hours and minutes of their pet's life, they may be asking their dog to support them once more, during this trauma. Their dog, who had the role of being the strong provider for their needs may attempt, against his better judgment, to struggle to stay as a comfort to them.

Staying may be stressful. Staying may be prolonging the time that the dog is experiencing pain. When it is time for your dog to transition, release him. Release your ties to your dog's spirit.

Give your dog permission to let go. Give your dog permission to move on to his/her spiritual journey.

Give your dog the full Transitions PetMassage we will describe in a few pages.

Although the techniques of PetMassage are helpful throughout every phase of an animal's life, they are especially powerful at the end of life. The tiny twitches, fits and jerks you see in your animal's body during massage and bodywork are actually mini-sobs. They do the same thing. They are release valves for overwhelmed emotional capacitors. They release emotionally hooked memories that have been stuck within their myofascial tissues.

If you are not comfortable working with your dog this way, perhaps you could sit with a professional PetMassage bodyworker as they provide the Transitions massage. You can watch. You can assist simply by being present.

The Transitions PetMassage was healing for Oskar and me. It will be for you, as well. A gentle therapeutic massage for yourself will give you the time and space for your own emotional processing. During a massage, it is not uncommon for an emotional moment to arise. You may begin to cry. Crying is a good thing. Crying is cleansing.

Sob

Have you ever had the experience of seeing some simple ritual, like lighting a candle, trigger a fit of convulsive sobbing? If you have, you know that afterwards you feel completely drained. You are emotionally exhausted; yet you are left with a feeling of immense relief, of lightness. Your memory file of "things that hurt but dealing with them was postponed," was repressed...trapped. And as long as it was there, you were stuck, too. They were crowding around in there, taking up valuable memory space, restricting your breathing and your capacities to feel and see, hear and reason. Increased emotional pressure increases stress, which either causes disease or at the very least, does not inhibit its progression and everything else that goes along with that unfortunate downward spiral.

To sob or not to sob is not a conscious decision. It is a primal reflex, sourced in the same region of the mind as the intuitive fight or flee response. The "rain barrel effect" occurs when your unconscious spiritual vessel gets filled and filled until there is no more room for more suppressed feelings. Then it overflows.

The flow is healthy. Continuing to stuff everything inside, isn't. Your internal intuitive body has its own way of releasing its burden of pent up memories and emotions. Bottom line: it's okay and healthy to cry. Another bottom line: you do not have a choice about it. When your spirit cries, you cry.

Mem'ries
It is healthy to remember too. If you are comfortable journaling, record some of your favorite memories of times shared with your dog. Allow yourself to be immersed in the good old familiar activities.

Children are encouraged to draw pictures of their pets; and this is a wonderfully cathartic process for adults, as well. Get out your crayons or markers and a couple of big sheets of blank paper and let your emotions flow. Infuse the drawings with words and phrases. Blue can be orange, brown can be pink. Let the colors run through your tears. Let the images flow through your laughter.

Dogs create art, too. The Picasso-esque design pictured above, "Equine on Wall," by our Standard poodle, Jacques, was created working with three paws on the ground and one in the air. Ah, artists!

We've learned that energy can neither be created nor destroyed. It changes form. As the life force ebbs away, in the void, a death force replaces it. What do you think happens when your dog transitions?

Death may be becoming part of a great emptiness or nothingness. It may not. It could be a reconnection with the pure spirit experience continuum. A spirit is immortal. It was there before birth, before inhabiting a body, it chose a life style. It chose to create an opportunity to teach some very valuable lessons and learn even more. Those lessons included experiencing and providing unconditional love.

Your dog's spirit chose to live with you. It placed itself where it could hang out with you and his other spiritual friends just as it had in the past and will in the future. You knew it when you saw it the first moment you were together. You have known it all of your existence. Your journeys will continue together another time. This is a description of soul mates.

Our pets and we are part of a magnificently huge, never ending pattern of revolving and evolving instruction and growth.

We always were, and in all ways are, forever together. With each other, we help one another evolve. Our energies are maneuvering us to achieve balance, harmony and completeness. We are together. We could not do it without each other's help. We complete each other.

Each of us has our own unique variation of source experience. Esther Hicks, the channeler of the collection of spiritual teachers called Abraham, used a phrase in one of her workshops that jumped out at me. Abraham, as channeled by Esther, describing the powerful, stream of intention and experience that got you started your life, used the phrase, "the source you rode in on." The source-force surrounds you and guides you. It is who you are. The source-force and its initial inertia propel you and help you to make course corrections along your path. It is the same life force that is known as Ch'i.

Esther used another metaphor that resonated with me. She intoned, "life force is a stream that enters this life river and gets swept away with it." The life force travels alone, sometimes with the flow, sometimes against it. Moving with the flow is easy and fun. Working against the flow is difficult and frustrating. That is why you feel a sense of bliss when you are doing something you love; and why doing what you enjoy is easy to do.

Deepak Chopra points our attention to the obvious, that when you're having a wonderful time you loose track of time. You are floating, carried with the river's current. Doing something you dislike is more difficult and seems to take forever to complete. This is moving against the current.

We begin our lives with a certain amount of streaming Ch'i. Ch'i can be enhanced with a healthy lifestyle or diminished by an unhealthy one. When it can no longer move on its own, Ch'i gets swept away in the big ethereal stream. Esther calls it simply, the Source. When the Ch'i is used up, death happens.

You'll know the source (horse) you rode in on very well. You'll recognize the comfortable fit and feel of the perfectly broken-in saddle, the perfect length of the stirrup leathers and the secure slope and size of the stirrups. The reins are ones you've always known and loved. The reins are extensions of your hands. Your fingers curl naturally and easily around them. The gentle rocking of your seat at the walk, the easy rhythm and rolling bounce of the trot or lope and the breathtaking absolute joyous rush, running flat out at top speed, have been, are, and will always be natural to you and a part of you.

Your spirit self is the movement. Your spirit self is the emotion. Your spirit self is the energy. Your pet's spirit self has the same life source.

After your pet dies, his reality isn't where you are. It is where he is. So, when your pet wakes up and finds himself in his old comfy boots, he'll dig his heels into his source and take off happily with the psychic yelp of "Yippee!" or "Yee-haw!" or "Yaw-hey!" Giddy screams of delight fill the universe over the steady back-beat of source hooves clopping on immortal Karmic cobblestones.

Have you ever had the real time, experience of listening to the howl of the wild wolf? Its feeling is more palpable than its sound. It is the closest experience of the sound of the universal ether we can have. Aakash.

Gesundheit.

The energy of the howl enters the body through the heart and the bowels, rather than through the ears. Sometimes the sound is lonely and plaintive; other times, it is powerful and all-knowing. The cognition of the sound makes one feel as if you were flowing down and around a psychic water slide. Timeless psychic screams fill your ears. They fill your body. They have the passion, wildness, joy and awareness of your complete connectedness to everything that is.

This could be what happens when your pet "dies" or "transitions." On this side is what we believe we know to be true. On the other side is something else. Hopefully, it is peace and joy, contentment and completeness.

The lessons that your dog had to share with you were taught. The lessons your dog had to learn were learned. You, your dog's co-travelers, partner in time, are still with them; now in a different, more perfect, more present form.

Your pet is no longer isolated in the time-lapse mechanism of being with you during periods of wakefulness and separated from you during sleep. Where he is, there is no need for sleep, so there is no sleep. Where he is, there is only presence. He has rejoined your spiritual side. At a profound level, you are closer than you know. Along with fellow spiritual travelers, you are both on your lazy hazy ride moving about the universe on their various sizes and shapes, colors and textures and vibrations of sources. Where are you all going? What are you all doing? In the story of *Peter Pan*, the way to Neverland is "first star to the left and straight on till morning."

In the Cervantes novel, *Don Quixote,* the final actions of the knight and his faithful squire, Sancho Panza, "thunder off in all directions, swinging at windmills and jousting with cows." Moving off in all directions simultaneously is entirely possible if you are not constricted by the earthbound limits of linear time and three dimensions of space.

You may feel that the spirit of your pet has separated itself from you and the world you live in. You may feel empty and angry; deserted, disappointed and hurt. You miss the joy he brought into your home and your life. You miss him and your connection with him.

His body, his earthly container, was mortal. Your pet may have been the victim of a random accident or genetic degeneration. While the body was broken, from trauma, disease, discomfort, or age, the spirit that was in it, continues to thrive.

Linear time only has relevance to those living in a finite state of consciousness. Groucho Marx has a famous quote. He said, "Outside of a dog, a book is man's best friend. Inside of a dog, it's too dark to read."

Outside of what we experience, time and space are irrelevant. Everything exists at once. Inside of life, it is too crowded with distractions to see it. Once his transition is made, your dog's spirit is always with you, everywhere, every time.

Even though you will always be together in the realm of energy bodies, as he progresses from this life to whatever is next, you can help your dog's physical self find its balance, harmony and peace. Final Transitions PetMassage$_{TM}$ is a tool to help you assist your pet "back in the saddle again."

PetMassage$_{TM}$ for dogs: final transition applications
The closing treatments are separated into 4 parts.

1 Palliative Care
    Including geriatric massage, relaxation massage, energy balancing, Mudras, snapping and the pain drain
2 Transitions PetMassage,
3 Euthanasia
4 Grief counseling for owners
    Including Pet Loss and Children
5 Grief support for surviving pets

1 Palliative Care
Palliative care refers to the end of life care where drugs and medical interventions are no longer effective and the patient is kept "comfortable" until the life force gives way to the death urge. The dictionary definition for "palliative" is: serving to relieve or alleviate, without curing. 2. An agent that alleviates or eases. (Encarta Dictionary)

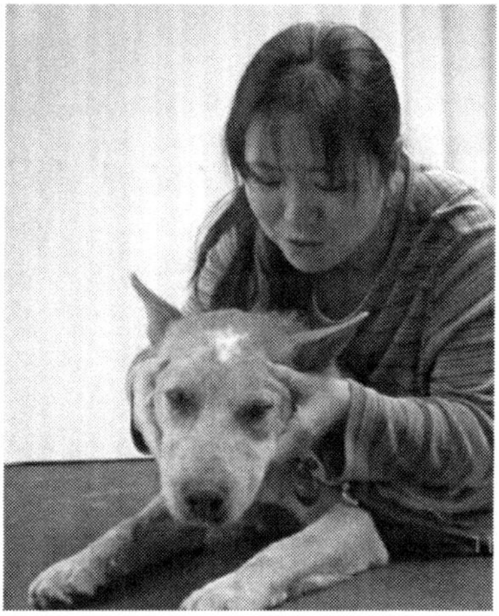

Animal massage and bodywork can be a profoundly powerful part of animal palliative care. Animals respond to the caring touch of their owners and other pets. Combining veterinary care and PetMassage is a loving way to support your dog.

PetMassage is one-on-one attention and nurturing. PetMassage calms and relaxes. It honors the whole animal, body, mind and spirit, so that your dog can live his/her life with dignity and comfort. We've seen how massage and bodywork helps animals create ambient inner environments where whatever medications that are administered, including the drugs used for pain management; will be more optimized by the body.

A PetMassage by the animal's guardian is a beautiful way to share love and affection. It is a way for a special person to give back to the pet some of the unconditional love they have been getting for as long as they have been together.

The geriatric PetMassage and relaxation PetMassage are two distinctly different massage forms.

The intention of the geriatric *PetMassage* is to increase circulation and restore the feeling of strength, comfort and control over physical and emotional circumstances.

The geriatric PetMassage includes gentle range of motion, stretching, and enthusiastic scratching on the spine, hips and shoulders. In also invokes lighter, lymphatic drainage, strokes. These lighter strokes are quick flicks, involving combing motions with your fingers directed against the lay of the hair, from the periphery of your dog's body, toward the heart.

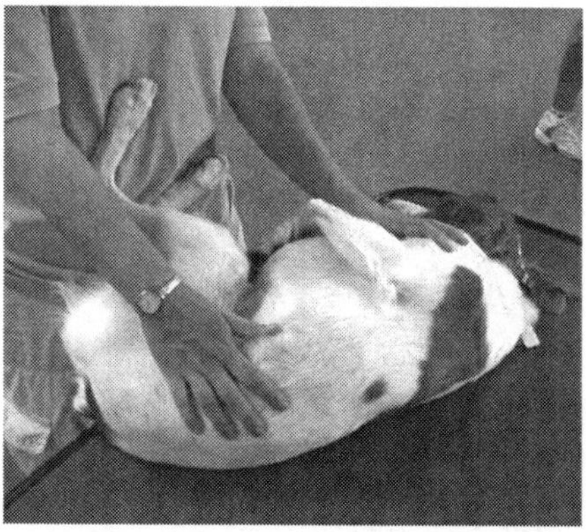

The relaxation PetMassage has the intention of generally allowing the body to experience and move toward its uniquely conceived, place of comfort.

Strokes of the relaxation PetMassage are slower, softer, and directed from the heart to the extremities. All of the movements have the character of staying well within the extremes of range of motion, yielding to the body's choices for comfort in movement. The range of motion that is demonstrated is more unintentional.

Each of the regions of fascia that encase compromised groups of muscles, limbs or joint capsules, is placed in a slightly restrictive position, allowing it to unwind.

During the process of unwinding, your dog's mind and spirit may have the chance to revisit, review and re-invent alternative ways of understanding their version of the truth for itself. Your dog's body has the opportunity to, once again, search for, and rediscover, its place of comfort.

The relaxation PetMassage is good therapy throughout your animal's life; it is a powerful method for older or impaired dogs of re-evaluation and body re-education.

Energy balancing is the ultimate goal of PetMassage. Intentional touch, stroking, skin and auric fascia rolling are all combined to assist the animal toward optimal energetic circulation.

Vectoring, holding the animal with two hands while focusing on the movement of his energy through his body, from one palm to the other, strengthens and connects the Ch'i flowing in, around, and through the body.

Gently cup the chest with one hand over the sternum, and place your other over the withers. Or place your hands on either side of the ribs just behind the elbows. You are creating vectors, or forces of influence, between your hands.

Envision the energy moving from one palm to the other, through the heart, pericardium, lungs and ribs.

Place one palm on either side of the hips. Envision the energy moving from one palm to the other, through the hips, pelvic girdle, and all the organs and tissues within it.

Vectoring techniques help you assess and assist in the movement of your pet's body's energy patterns. With practice your vectoring will become stronger and more activating.

Notice that when you stroke over your pet's body, your hands move at different rates. Why would this be?

Some areas may feel clean and empty, in which case your hands will move easily onto and away from the body. Other areas may feel heavy and thick. The body space is exerting an unusual drag or resistance. To pull your hand away you have to exert more effort, as if you were slogging through surf or combing your fingers through a tangled horse's mane. The clean and empty feeling is free-flowing, healthy, and vibrant. The heavy thick sensation describes stagnation, where the life force is stuck or impaired.

Through vectoring, you are palpating the textures, and the implicit behaviors, of the auric fields around your dog. Now that you can perceive subtle variations in the body field, you can do something about it.

Your fingers can not only detect; they can also be useful in directing fields' characteristics to help restore their balance and comfort. Your fingers hold innate powers in them that you may not have been aware of. Each of the five elements: fire, air, earth, water, and spirit, is triggered by individual fingers. Five fingers for five elements.

The physical body is made up of five elements namely - Air, Water, Fire, Earth and Aakash (ether - the tiny intercellular spaces in the human body). In China, qigong practitioners, in India, Ayurvedic practitioners, in Native America, aboriginal medicine guides, and in every culture for millennia, there have been nature-oriented health practitioners who have understood that deficiencies in any of these elements cause disease and discomfort. These natural healthcare practition-ers discovered that these deficiencies can be rebalanced through systematically connecting one part of the body with another. Finger positions that connect representative elements in a particular manner are called mudras. The finger

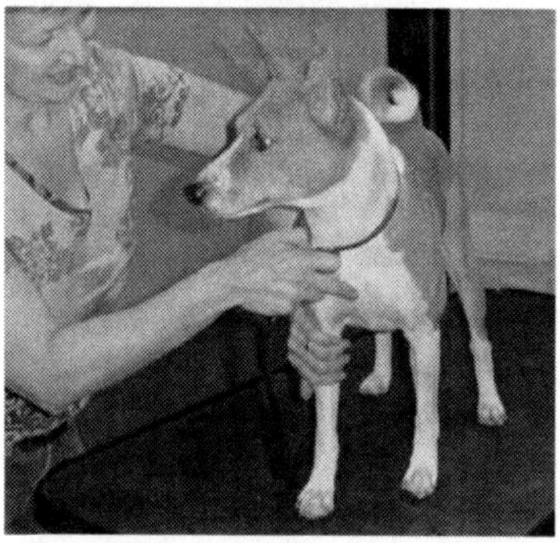

elements correspond to the elements of the Traditional Chinese Meridian ting points.

Mudras start electromagnetic currents within the body which balance various constituting elements and restore health. The joining of fingers creates an effect on the human body.

This is the pattern of the fingers and their corresponding elements. (See Mudras, Appendix III)

- Thumb: Fire
- Index finger: Air
- Middle finger: Aakash
- Ring finger: Earth
- Little finger: Water

A way to remember which goes with which is: Thumb, I touch the handle of a hot skillet with my thumb, fire. I hold my index finder up in the air to check which way the wind is blowing, air. My middle finder is the longest and the strong pole that points to heaven; it supports and stabilizes the rest of the hand, Aakash. My ring finger represents grounding, family and stability, earth. My little finger is the one I dipped into my infant daughter's bath to make sure the temperature was perfect, water.

Imbalance of these elements disrupts the immunity system and causes discomfort disturbance, and, disease. When a finger representing an element is brought into contact with the thumb, that element is set afire, triggered and stimulated to move back toward balance.

Since dogs do not have opposable thumbs, they cannot connect their mudras on their own.

Stimulate the individual toes, around the sides of the cuticles. Notice the textures of the tissues. They can be soft, hard, mushy, dry, raised or hollowed. Notice if the nail is torn or bruised. Many dogs are sensitive and have unpleasant memories connected with having their nails trimmed. Part of their anger may stem from the lack of regard for the mudra characteristics associated with the individual toes. Help them restore their connections by gently squeezing the toes with your thumb and middle finger, the same fingers you snap with. Notice your dog's reactions to your touch. As you practice this part of the PetMassage, notice if your dog is more accepting and responsive.

The "snap" is the PetMassage$_{TM}$ variation on the mudra that presses the tip of the middle finger to the base of the thumb. Snapping the thumb (fire) against the Middle finger (Aakash) helps to jump start, stimulate, stagnant energy.

When your dog's body is surrounded by a strong force field, it is withdrawing into its energy cave. You will feel a field of thick, repulsive resistance around him.

To assist him with PetMassage, first ask and get his permission to work in his body-field. Initially, you may feel that you cannot access it, since it is encased in energetic armoring.

Begin with off the body vectoring, until you are permitted to place you hands on his coat. In addition to all the things that we discussed, vectoring empowers dogs to pay attention to their body space. When your dog has given you his permission, gently snap your fingers two or three times in the region that you sensed was stagnant or stuck.

Retest the area for any noticeable changes before each series of snaps by scanning with your palms. Your centers of your palms are the part of your hands that are the most sensitive to heat and pressure.

You will soon notice the areas are less restrictive and be able to move to them and away from them more easily. If necessary, repeat the snap sequence two or three times.

There are no contraindications for the snap. You cannot snap too many times, snap too hard, or cause new problems. Your dog will intuitively ignore whatever is not in his best interests. He will accept whatever you offer him that he can use. The worst case scenario is he becomes annoyed by your quick movements and the sound of snapping fingers.

Assisting the release of discomfort is helpful when you sense that your dog is in physical or emotional pain. The pain drain connects to the area of perceived discomfort, pulls it away from the body and allows it to drain off your other hand back into the earth.

How do you know where the discomfort is? Your dog is telling you he is feeling discomfort when you bring your hand close to his body, or touch his body lightly, and he responds with a yipe, a squeal, a snap, a pull away, a tensing up of muscles, or if he holds his breath or winces.

Technique: Place one hand over the region on the body where you sense stuckness and stagnation. Snap up the indiscretion. Visualize the energy that is loaded with discomfort flowing into your palm, up your arm, across your shoulders, down your extended arm and out through your fingertips into the earth. Your hand is a grounding wire that helps your pet recalibrate his internal "channels."

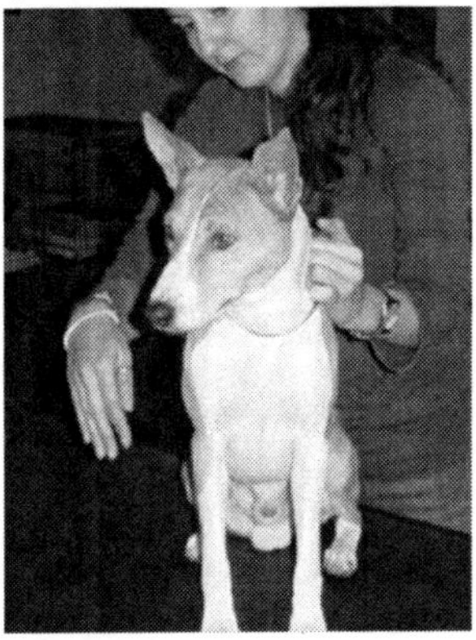

This method creates drain channels for stress, emotional and physical discomfort and negativity. Allow its energy to flow out your other hand, fingers directed off toward the ground. Redirecting your dog's stagnant energy supports the release of stiffness, discomfort and distressing anxieties. It will help you to help your dog to simply cope.

Observe how your own body feels. Along with your dog's discomfort, some of the excess negativity and pain that you've been holding may drain off, out and away, as well.

There is no need to replace it with "positive" energy. The drain is a process that creates balance. The drain enhances energy flow by removing obstructions. In this case, the obstructions were thick, stagnant energy.

Complete by vectoring, reestablishing your connections with both hands on your dog's body. Visualize the flow of the dog's Ch'i energy through your palms once more. See it moving with more joy and vitality through the areas where you had perceived the obstructions.

Make sure you are well grounded before and after performing the pain drain, so that you do not take on your dog's discomfort, anxieties, etc. You might be a little embarrassed later in the day to find yourself exhibiting some of his behaviors, like hip soreness or needing to mark every tree or not being able to hear someone calling your name while you are busy chasing squirrels.

2 Transitions PetMassage

The Transitions PetMassage form celebrates your pet's life. It honors and celebrates its natural processes. The Transitions PetMassage stimulates, satisfies and opens the energetic patterns in and around his body. It offers direction for your pet's life force. It provides permission and support for it to move gracefully into the experience of whatever is next.

The Transitions PetMassage incorporates touch, intention, compassion, trust and awareness of the stillness/motion of the Aakasha.

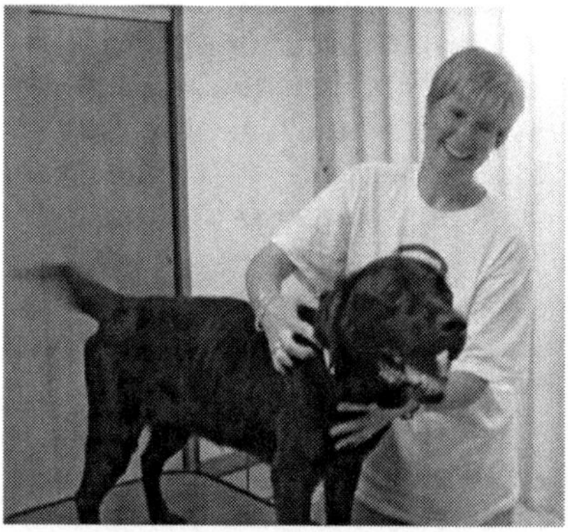

To begin, calm yourself by observing and controlling your breathing.

Become grounded. Feel yourself rooted through the floor.

Channel whatever you sense as the flow of dog life force. Engage your dog's energy patterns and reinforce them by following the specific sequence of vectors, the series of connecting double points on the dog's body. Be the witness for the flow of energy moving through the tissues from one of your palms to the other.

As your dog follows the movements of your hands on his body, his deeper intention is pulled in. Intention follows attention.

Slowly and mindfully enhance your dog's total body awareness with the full series of assessment strokes on his body. (See: *Effective Pet Massage for Dogs, Manual*, "Assessment strokes") Keeping your hands relaxed; use your fingers and palms to stroke completely over his face, ears and head. Spend a little extra time to gently stimulate the tissues in and around the bases of the ears and around the eyes and nose.

With your dog's permission unzip his auric body field, slicing the tips of your connected thumb and middle finger above and through the midline of his auric body bag from nose to tail, cranial to caudal.

Use both hands to gently comb through the aura splaying and separating the layers of the shells laterally from the midline toward the sides. Repeat this motion two or three times. When you are at this point, as long as you stay open and present, your dog's intuition for his greatest good will guide your hands. You may feel that you need to move further away from the body with each pass. You may feel you need to move closer to his body. You may need to move slower or faster. Follow your intuition.

Visualize your dog's energy field open.

Maintain contact with his body with your non-dominant hand, called your mother hand, and dip into the energy within the body space with the other, your active hand. Stir up the body space using a scooping motion with your active hand. Visualize the twisting vapors of steam climbing into the air. Allow it to float and drift away from the body space. Observe how it moves, twisting and turning as it absorbs and draws away any of your dog's discomfort, confusion, regrets, missed opportunities, and negative memories.

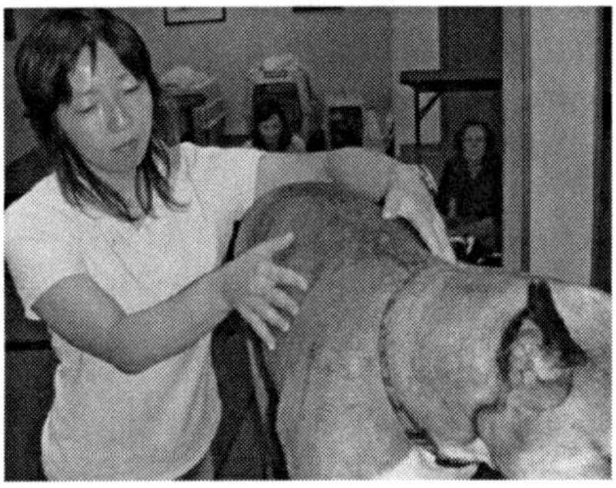

Your hands and fingers may feel tingly, stinging, or have some sensation that you have no words to describe. Feel the energy move up your arm and into your chest. Direct it down your spine, legs and observe it as it flows out of you, through your feet and deep into the ground. Take a breath, refresh your self with new air and clean Aakashic energy.

Release expectations and attachments to the outcome. Your dog, with your influence and support, is moving toward his greatest good naturally and easily. Breathe love and contentment back into the body space.

It is perfectly acceptable to express your emotions during the PetMassage. Give yourself permission to cry. Allow cleansing tears to flow. Your true voice comes not from your throat and mind; rather, from your heart and soul. If you are fortunate enough to enter into thc uncontrollable, full body sob, surrender completely. Relish the moment. This is your transition, too.

Convulsive body spasms release stifled trapped emotions. When they are diminished, you will move freely into your own next phase.

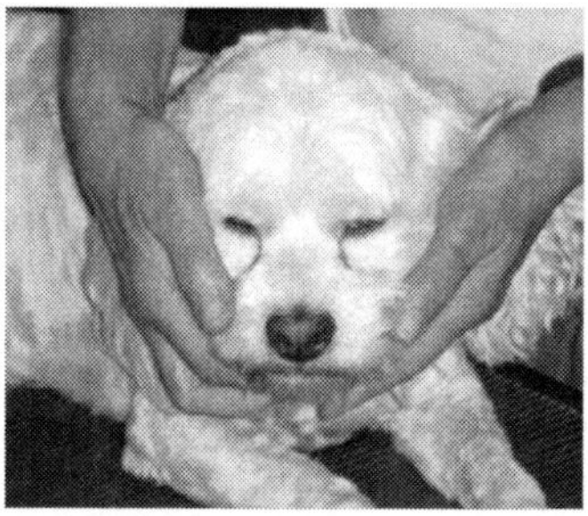

Observe your breathing to regroup and quiet yourself. You had been working on your own issues; and that's okay. Now, you can reconnect with your dog.

As you reestablish in your mind that you are in a safe and secure place, your dog moves with you. He is sharing in your emotional journey.

If this is his end of life Transitions PetMassage, do not rezip the seams of your dog's body space. Allow it to continue in this open position.

Sit quietly together, enjoying each others company. Allow the memories your time together to flow past your eyes. Experience the emotions you shared, one last time. Your emotions elicit subtle alterations in your hormones, which in turn affect the bouquet of aromas of your perspiration. Your dog will follow your thoughts by knowing how each of them smell! Recall your time together; the good times, the stressful times and especially the average, non eventful times that made up 99.9 percent of your life together.

There is no need to ground the dog after the PetMassage. We want to encourage him/her to follow-on with a natural procession of end of life releases.

To complete the session, gently trace over the crest of the scull running over the top from the eyes to the top of the neck with your fingers. Lightly squeeze the tips of each of the toes at the base of the nails and trace the swirl of hair over the sternum, breastbone. That is it. You are complete.

After the session, you may feel that you are in an altered state. You are. Ground yourself after the session by thoroughly washing your hands, taking a walk and eating a piece of fresh fruit.

What have you just done? Was it alright? Whose interests were served? Was it about your dog or you? Let go of your attachments to any outcomes. The only expectation you can have is that your dog is moving toward and into his greatest good. That is the intention that you must keep foremost in your mind. And "good," as my friend, Mary Jean says, "is good enough."

3 Euthanasia

We and our pets are fortunate that we can also choose alternative methods of supporting and allowing a pet to die. Keeping a dog alive for as long as possible through medications, chemotherapies and respirators is one way of supporting our dog at the time of his transition. This may not be your best choice. Keeping your dog alive at all costs may not be in his best interest.

Quantity of life is not the same as quality of life. It is always painful to make a choice that determines whether or not a pet will live or move on to his unknown and unknowable destination. When your pet has worn out his body, or continuing medical interventions is destroying his quality of life, it is time to be proactive in allowing his spirit, or soul, to be released from its present condition. Euthanasia may be the most loving, humane choice.

In my experience, as a registered nurse I have seen too many people kept alive who were ready and eager to move on. Families of human patients are not allowed the humane option for their loved ones to pass away quickly, painlessly and with dignity.

The process is invariably degrading for the patient. This is not the fittingly honorable end for a vital, loving and valuable life. Sitting the death vigil can be a horrific experience for the dying person's family, who, in the face of cultural confusion, must convince themselves that their actions are moral and appropriate.

We need to ask the questions: Where are our priorities? Who determines what is right and just? Do we as a culture question how has death been taught to us? What could have the motivations been behind the teachings?

A quick, painless death with its quiet disengagement and peace is a beautiful experience when compared to the alternative; a death of drug muffled pain and hopelessness.

The euthanasia experience with Oskar was dignified, as befitting a prince of his status. We may have been able to keep him alive for a few more days or weeks. It would be a painful struggle for everyone involved. After his transition, Anastasia and I sat and talked. We thought we might feel remorse, or sadness, regrets or tearfulness. We had no second thoughts. We discovered that we felt elated. We had decided wisely in Oskar's best interest. He was now free of a painful and dysfunctional body. We had released a part of our physical selves that had been broken and stuck. Our spiritual personae, including Oskar, are still intact. It was a very good thing we did.

4 Grief counseling for owners

There was a young woman who had a dog who was 12 years old and in considerable discomfort. He could no longer move about by himself. He could barely eat without assistance. This was her best friend, her confidant, her teacher, her witness and advisor in all things. She was the only one who could make the decision.

After several days of praying to know what to do, she told her dog that on Monday morning she was taking him to the vet to have him put down. Oh, how she cried. Her dog understood. The Sunday evening before the appointment, as she held him, he passed quietly in his sleep. Permission and acceptance are complete.

It was about setting their intentions and having an agreement on a soul level. This story is common. You've probably heard many other versions of it.

Grief is a normal response to any important loss in life. It occurs regardless of whether death followed a prolonged illness, or a sudden accident. Grieving people experience both physical and emotional traumas as they try to adapt to the upheaval in their lives brought about by the loss.

The grief suffered by pet owners after their pet dies is the same as that experienced after the death of a person. A pet, even more than another person, leaves behind a gaping hole in the owners daily living patterns. With a pet, every moment is consciously shared. Suddenly, there is no longer anything for the pet owner to nurture and care for. And, the owner looses his or her contact with "the natural world."

These feelings can be particularly intense for the elderly, single people and childless couples for whom the pet also is a child substitute.

The grief process is ongoing. Each person experiences it in a different way. Dividing the grief process in to "stages" helps the grief stricken person to understand that their experiences and emotions are normal. Some people will quickly progress through all the phases, while others appear to get "stuck" in a particular phase. Briefly, these are the stages of grief:

The Stages of Grief

1. SHOCK AND DENIAL- The reality of death has not yet been accepted by the bereaved. He or she feels stunned and bewildered-as if everything is "unreal."
2. ANGER- The grief stricken person often lashes out at family, friends, themselves, God, the veterinarian or the world in general. Bereaved people will also experience feelings of guilt or fear during this stage.
3. BARGAINING- In this stage, the bereaved asks for a deal or reward from either God, the veterinarian or the Clergy. Comments like "I'll go to Church every day, if only my pet will come back to me" are common.
4. DEPRESSION- Depression occurs as a reaction to the changed way of life created by the loss. The bereaved person feels intensely sad, hopeless, drained and helpless. The pet is missed and thought about constantly.
5. ACCEPTANCE- Acceptance comes when the changes brought upon the person by the loss are stabilized into a new lifestyle. The depth and intensity of the mourning process depends on many factors. The age of the owner, circumstances surrounding the death, relationship of the animal to the owner and to other family members, are all significant. Recently experiencing the death of a significant person in the owner's life can also affect how the pet's death is handled. Usually, children recover more quickly, while the elderly take the longest. Sometimes, the death of a pet will finally enable the bereaved to mourn the loss of a person, whose death had not yet been accepted.

Once the acceptance stage has arrived, it is time to find another relationship. So many times, I have heard the sentiment, “I had a great dog named (name) twenty years ago. I could *never* get another dog. I could never find another (name). I don’t think I could go through another dog dying. It was just too hard on me.”

My response is, "You have so much love to share. You are right. You'll never find another one exactly like the one you lost. Now, you can have another relationship with a dog with a different, and amazing, personality. Think of the alternative. How dismal it must be to live without a dog's companionship! Right now, there is a dog looking for a person just like you. Go on and find him/her."

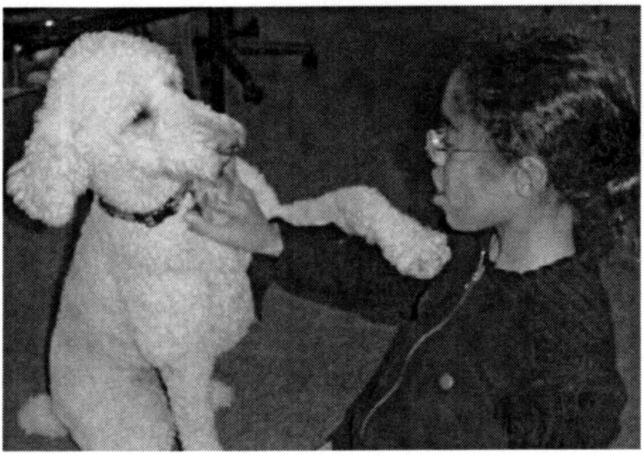

Pet Loss and Children

Death is traumatic and confusing for a child. Their grief is no less intense than that experienced by adults. Children also tend to come back to the subject repeatedly; so extreme patience is required when dealing with the grieving child. Some helpful tips for helping the grieving child include:

1. Give the child permission to work through their grief. ---
   - tell their teacher about the pet's death.
   - encourage the child to talk freely about the pet.
   - give the child plenty of hugs and reassurance.
   - discuss death, dying and grief honestly.
2. NEVER say things like "God took your pet," or the pet was "put to sleep."

- The child will learn to fear that God will take them, their parents or their siblings.
- The child may become afraid of going to sleep.

3. Include the child in everything that is going on.
4. Explain the permanency of death as best you can.

There is an excellent book by Mr. (Fred) Rogers entitled, *When a Pet Dies*, that is a guide for helping children with pet loss.

5 Grief support for surviving pets

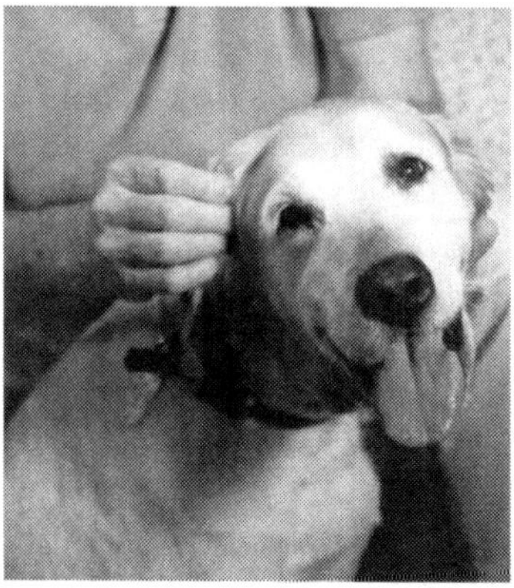

Pets grieve, too.

They often display the behaviors of the grief experience when they are moved from one home to another. New sights and sounds and smells are foreign and disorienting; definitely non-routine. When dogs grieve, they can display similar sorts of behaviors as people experiencing loss.

Dogs, find comfort in routine. When something in their environment changes, such as their food, or a teenager moving away to attend college, or another family dog leaving, they often grieve the comfort of knowing what was happening around them.

When we adopted our standard poodle, our boxer, Oskar grieved the loss of being a single dog. He missed the sights, the sounds, smells and all the wonderful human contact that made up the stuff of his old only-dog life. For two weeks, Oskar steadfastly ignored the three month old puppy's existence.

Oskar remained aloof, even though the puppy was continuously pouncing on him, taking his toys and eating out of his bowl. Then one day, Oskar had a breakthrough. He decided it was time to move on. He turned toward the little one who was nonchalantly playing about fifteen yards away, and charged at him full speed bowling him over. For the next five years, until Oskar's death, they were inseparable best friends.

Animal members of the family are dramatically affected when there is a cloud of grief descending on the household. Animals are keenly aware of the emotional dynamics in a household. They pay close attention to our subliminal body language cues, such as moving slowly, not standing up straight, sitting or pacing, eating less or more, lethargy, and malaise.

Dogs in general have a nose approximately a hundred thousand to a million times more sensitive than a human's. They pay close attention to any odors that we exude. Our emotions affect the concentration and chemistry of the sweat we produce.

The chemical content of our perspiration varies with the emotions we are experiencing. We have different aromas when we are healthy or sick, awake or tired, confident or fearful, sexually stimulated or disinterested, and especially happy, compared to grieving and sad. As much as we might like to think that we can hide our feelings from the world, our dogs have the ability to know our innermost thoughts and feelings.

Pets' attachments with each other are often very strong. They too feel the loss of a companion. Even pets that outwardly seem to barely get along will exhibit intense stress reactions when separated.

The hole in their lives can often be comforted and encouraged with PetMassage and bodywork. They too can achieve some closure on their feelings. They too appreciate the assistance to move on with their lives.

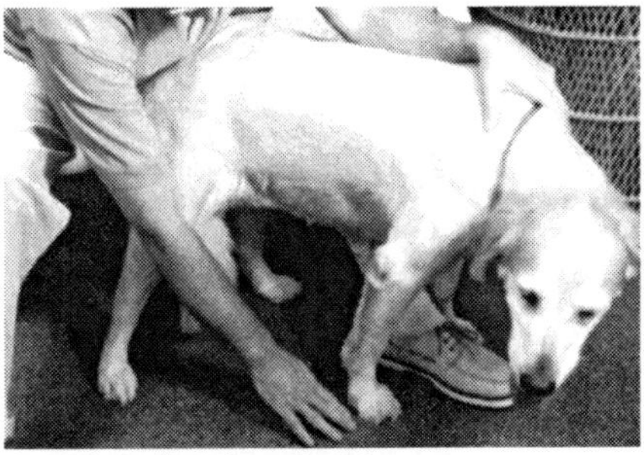

Gracie before her PetMassage

Gracie, pictured here, the lab-mix who was the recipient of the Geriatric PetMassage in the video, *Effective PetMassage™ for Older Dogs,* is a good example.

Before her PetMassage, Gracie was a Velcro-dog. She stayed so close to her owner that she was often touching her owner's side. Gracie's eyes were dull. Her tail hung listlessly. Her head was carried low and her nose was down below her elbows. Gracie's coat was dull and appeared rough and poorly clipped. Her breathing was shallow. Her movements were slow, disinterested and lethargic.

After her PetMassage, her head was up, her ears pricked and forward, her eyes were alert and bright, her tail was up and wagging. Gracie panted freely. The corners of her mouth were pulled up into a smile.

Somewhere in the 30 or so minutes that we shared the PetMassage experience, she was able to work through what had been troubling her.

Earlier that week, Gracie's family companion of 9 years, another retriever, had been euthanized. Gracie had been grieving.

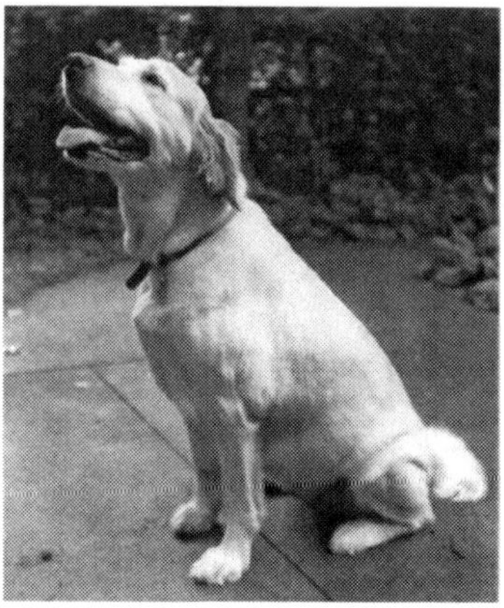
Gracie after her PetMassage

Gracie showed many symptoms identical to those experienced by bereaved pet guardians.

These were some of the signs that Gracie displayed while grieving:

1) Reduced energy, appearing listless
2) Tire more easily
3) They sleep more, spending more time in their "caves"
4) Lose appetite, lose weight
5) Coats become dull (with reduced circulation)
6) Eyes lose their brightness (with reduced interest)
7) Head, ears and tail hang loosely
8) They become more needy, having to be close or in contact most of the time; Velcro dogs
9) They also go through stages of grief similar to humans. They often progress to anger and acting out, resignation and usually, acceptance.

Often, grieving pets will search for their dead companions and crave more attention from their owners.

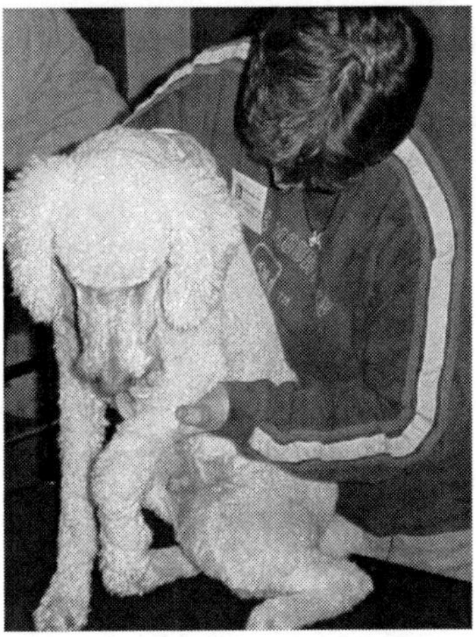

Summary

You have an important role to play at the end of your dog's life. Your state of intention affects the entire range of your pet's body, mind and spirit experience. The unique qualities of your presence and support are tremendously valuable.

The end of an animal's life is as important and essential a part of his/her existence as the rest of the life. Just as the puppy stage, the adolescent stage, the adult stage and the senior stage were progressions that we naturally observed and accepted, so too, is the end of life as we know it.

The end of life needs to be treated with the same respect, support, understanding and unconditional love as was given during the rest of the life.

During each stage, use PetMassage to enhance your dog's ability and willingness to function. Support and facilitate his end of life process, his transition from this plane of existence to whatever's next.

Relax and nurture the dog with PetMassage. As you quietly and calmly move through the sequences of vector holds, as you confidently and methodically stroke over your dog's entire body, he follows your touch. He experiences his body through the filter of your compassion, your grace. The Transitions PetMassage is a slow, mindful massage. It will help you and your dog resolve memories or resistance connections within your combined mind-body matrixes, so that your spirits can be released.

Use PetMassage to support the other surviving members of your family, including your pets. Remember that your friend's death was a natural part of the progression of life.

We humans get swept up in the emotional whirlpools of the circumstances in our lives. Sometimes when a pet is in the last stages of life, we need a support system more than ever. What happens if your pet is your support system?

You may have been relying on your dog for emotional support for many years, in the final hours and minutes of your pet's life, you may once more still be asking your dog to support you.

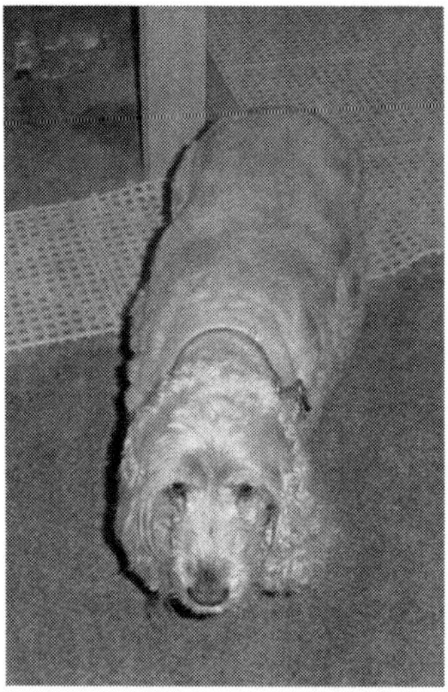

During this time of extreme trauma, your dog, who has had the role of being the provider for your needs may attempt, against his own better judgment, to struggle to stay to comfort you.

Staying may be stressful. Staying may be prolonging the time that the dog is experiencing pain. Give your dog the permission to let go; permission to move on to his/her spiritual journey.

Other animal members of the family may be affected by the cloud of grief that descends on the household. They too can be comforted with PetMassage and with your support, encouraged to move on with their lives.

The best gift your can give your dogs is to relax and nurture yourself. They feed off your emotions. Would you rather have them eat a diet of stress or a diet of comfort? You now have the skills. You have the choice.

You are following a path that allows your deepest feeling of respect and connection for all living things to surface and proliferate. Your deep sense of empathy and compassion are the keys for making this PetMassage, and any massage, effective.

You have learned important tools including intention, heightening your awareness, the specific hand movements and sequences.

You come to PetMassage with an appreciation for its potential.

Your power is in your love.

Your power is in your presence.

Your power is in your PetMassage touch.

APPENDIX I

Hospice care for dogs By: Marlene Grass, RVT, CMT, www.PetPlace.com

Bringing a pet into our lives is a joyful and rewarding experience. As people continue to embrace the giving spirit of the animal, we take on ethical and moral considerations; they are a part of our family.

The concept that an animal is "property," "just a dog" is no longer accepted by many people. When a pet becomes chronically or terminally ill, whether with cancer, immune diseases, kidney disease, liver disease, diabetes or other ailments, some difficult decisions need to be made. Some people feel that euthanasia is the best alternative.

However, the number of people who prefer to help ease their pet through the remainder of their days is growing. These individuals feel that it is not their choice to end a life. Instead, they would rather care for their pet, provide support and allow their companion to gracefully pass away. This type of care, referred to as hospice, has been common in the human health field for many years.

It is now becoming more and more accepted in our pets.

Caring for the terminally and critically ill can entail numerous tasks. The concept of hospice care has historically been thought of in connection with people. Many centers around the country and the world have been established through the human health care system to deliver hospice and palliative care. This care is done in conjunction with doctors and nurses in a facility for the aged, hospital or in a private residence. With the family acting as caregiver, the person is aided in the basics, grooming and appearance, exercise and physical therapy, nutrition and feeding, medication, fluid therapies, pain acknowledgement and remedy and general quality of life. This knowledge of hospice care is now being applied to our animal companions. Care for your pet, provide support and allow him/her to gracefully pass away. This type of care, referred to as hospice, has been common in the human health field for many years. It is now becoming more and more accepted in our pets.

Once the decision is made not to immediately perform euthanasia, the owner of the pet is then responsible for providing care. The owner or caregiver is not alone in this activity. Their support is the veterinary community, friends and neighbors. The veterinarian is available for examination, consultation and to prescribe and administer medical treatment. They may or may not make house calls. The veterinary technician is available to continue medical protocols, and to assist in the recognition of changes in the patient. The veterinary technician (nurse) can assist the caregiver of the terminally ill in many facets. With hospice care the quality of the pet's life is carefully monitored.

Palliative care is concerned with relieving pain. In the terminally and chronically ill pain relief can make the difference as to whether the pet and the caregiver can manage. There are some pain relief medications that only the veterinarian or the nurse will be allowed to administer directly to the patient. The caregiver can give other medication alone. The quality of life not only involves medication, but other therapeutic needs. The activity level and ability of the patient is also of great concern. If the pet is not active and cannot move, roll over or walk, assistance is needed. Different walkers and lifting slings, boots, harnesses and water therapies, aid the patient and the caregiver in movement. Movement of the pet helps to stop bedsores or pressure sores, fluid build up in the lungs and fluid accumulation in the limbs. Physical therapy that may include range of motion, passive joint movement, massage or aqua therapy, are most often more productive with a certified therapist or practitioner, than done alone by the caregiver. Playtime is also needed (no matter how delicate the pet is) in order to keep him alert. Changes in the routine can cause anxiety and behavior changes for all involved.

The patient needs to eat. Often, more calories are needed to maintain the body and mind of an ill pet than a healthy one. There are many ways to give nutrition to the terminally ill: feeding tubes of various kinds, hand feeding and syringe feeding, take time and need cleaning frequently. Some pets may need to be fed elevated or in a standing position, to aid them in acquiring the food and for digestion. Often the caregivers cannot do this by themselves. Different types of diets, or liquids (manufactured or homemade), or a combination of them are given.

Grooming is an often overlooked aspect of hospice care. A bath, nail trimming, brushing the teeth and cleaning the ears, eye and nose can help the pet feel better. Removing hair mats and trimming long hair will improve their attitude. Many pets have a difficult time going outside to urinate and defecate. These pets need diligent cleaning and protection against urine scalding. These things do not sound extremely pressing in light of the circumstances, but they are to your loved one.

Your pet's sleeping or living area may need to be supported with cushions or pads. Elevated beds, beds on the floor, and beds that may have heat, water or air circulating can help them maintain a certain body temperature and increase their circulation. Certain types of padding will help control incontinence problems.

The area in which the patient's bed is located is also important. A pet that has been active and spends the majority of his time in the midst of the family should continue to do so. A bed placed out of the way can tend to be detrimental to the pet's well-being. This will allow other family members to visit frequently. The interaction between pets in a multi animal home is still very important and should be somewhat supervised, just like with children.

This is a brief idea of some of the concerns that hospice care entails. Taking the responsibility to care for the terminally ill can take a toll on the caregiver as well. Build a support network and talk to them often. Find a veterinarian willing to assist in hospice care. Allow a hospice veterinary nurse (certified technician) to help you care for your pet. Watching for respiratory, digestive and neurologic concerns with your pet, as well as administering medications, exercising, grooming, feeding, etc., is overwhelming. But not impossible! You are not alone.

APPENDIX II

This article is by Margaret Muns, DVM. She is a staff veterinarian on the Best Friends Animal Sanctuary forum.

Here are some recommendations of things that an owner can do to help their grieving pets.

1. Keep the surviving pet(s) routines as normal as possible.
2. Try not to unintentionally reinforce the behavior changes. If the pet's appetite is picky, don't keep changing the food. All that does is create a more finicky pet. Don't over do the attention given to the pet(s) as it can lead to separation anxiety.
3. Allow the surviving animals to work out the new dominance hierarchy themselves. There may be scuffles and fights as the animals work out the new pecking order (dogs mostly).
4. Don't get a new pet to help the grieving pet(s) unless the owner is ready. It will backfire unless the owner is emotionally ready for a new pet. People still grieving won't have the energy for it.

Should the owner let the surviving animals see and smell their dead companion? There is no clinical evidence that doing so will help the surviving pet(s), but some people claim that it does. We know that all thoughts and emotions have frequencies, as sound and chemical characteristics including aroma. The animal will smell the spontaneous tissue decay. He will also smell the absence of the familiar thoughts, emotions and energy patterns that had been there before. Therefore, if the owner wants to have the surviving pets "say good-bye," then it should be allowed.

Even if all it accomplishes is to make the owner feel better, this in itself is a valid reason. For, when the owner is more comfortable, she will be sharing her level of comfort with her pet. Her pet will is highly sophisticated in the ability to perceive and interpret all its accompanying frequencies, chemicals and aromas.

Healing:
Given time, healing will occur for the bereaved owner. However, there are several things that the grief stricken owner can do to help speed up the healing process:

1. Give yourself permission to grieve. Only YOU know what your pet meant to you.
2. Memorializing your pet makes the loss real and helps with closure. Allow yourself to express your feelings, pay tribute and reflect.
3. Get lots of rest, good nutrition and exercise.
4. Surround yourself with people who understand your loss. Let others care for you.
5. Learn all you can about the grief process. This helps you realize that what you are experiencing is normal.
6. Accept the feelings that come with grief. Talk, write, sing, or draw.
7. Indulge yourself in small pleasures. Get a massage.
8. Be patient with yourself. DON'T let society dictate how long mourning should last.
9. Give yourself permission to backslide. It WILL end and your life WILL be normal again. Grief is like waves in the ocean: at first the waves come in fast and hard, but as time goes on, the waves become less intense and further apart. Don't be surprised if holidays, smells, sounds, or words trigger a relapse.
10. Don't be afraid to get help. Pet loss support groups, grief counselors...
11. Be sure to consult your own "Higher Power." Either religious or spiritual.

Grief is probably the most confusing, frustrating and emotional thing that a person can experience. It is even more so for pet owners. Society in general does not give bereaved pet owners "permission" to grieve openly. Consequently, pet owners often feel isolated and alone. Luckily, more and more resources are becoming available to help the bereaved pet owner realize that they are NOT alone and that what they are feeling is entirely normal.

APPENDIX III Additional Information about **Mudras**

Mudras are gestures or positions, usually of the hands, that lock and guide energy flow and reflexes to the brain. By curling, crossing, stretching and touching the fingers and hands, we can talk to the body and mind as each area of the hand reflexes to a certain part of the mind or body.

In each mudra, exert enough pressure to feel the flow of energy through the "nadis" (psychic channels) up the arms but not enough to whiten fingertips.

(Ref. -Guru Rattana, Ph.D., *Transitions to a Heart Centered World*)

Some commonly used mudras are:

GUYAN MUDRA: The tip of the thumb touches the tip of the index finger, stimulating knowledge and ability. The index finger is symbolized by Jupiter, and the thumb represents the ego. Guyan Mudra imparts receptivity & calm.

ACTIVE GUYAN MUDRA: The first joint of the index finger is bent under the first joint of the thumb, imparting active knowledge.

SHUNI MUDRA: Tip of middle finger (symbolized by Saturn) touches the tip of the thumb, giving patience.

SURYA or RAVI MUDRA: Tip of the ring finger (symbolized by Uranus or the Sun) touches the tip of the thumb, giving energy, health and intuition.

BUDDHI MUDRA: Tip of little finger (Mercury) touches tip of thumb for clear and intuitive communication.

VENUS LOCK: Interlace fingers with left little finger on the bottom, with the right index finger on top for men and the left for women. The Venus mounds at the base of the thumbs are pressed together channeling sensuality and sexuality, and glandular balance, helping to focus and concentrate.

JUPITER MUDRA: With the two index fingers together, the power of Jupiter, or good luck and expansion is activated. Together they focus your energy to break through barriers.

PRAYER MUDRA: Palms are pressed together, neutralizing and balancing yin & yang, for centering.

BEAR GRIP: Left palm faces out from body with thumb down, and right palm faces body, thumb up, and fingers are curled and hooked together to stimulate the heart and intensify concentration.

BUDDHA MUDRA: Right hand rests on left for men, left on right for women, palms up, thumbs tips touching each other in a receptive gesture.

Mudras for Benefits:
Gyan Mudra Effective in cases of mental ailment, imparts happiness, the intellect develops, memory is sharpened **Method** Join the tips of the index finger and thumb and keep the other 3 fingers stretched and joined.
Shoonya Mudra Relief in diseases and pains relating to the ear **Method** Press the middle finger on the base of the thumb and keep the thumb on middle finger. Keep the other three fingers straight.
Apaan Mudra Helps in clearing the body by elimination of waste matter from the mouth, eyes, ears, nose etc. Helps when urine is obstructed, reduces constipation. **Method** Join the tip of the thumb with the tip of middle and ring finger, keeping the other fingers straight.
Prana Mudra Helps in pumping the life force into your body. Beneficial for all types of diseases. Imparts special power to the eyes. **Method** Join the tip of the thumb with tip of little and ring finger. Keeping other two fingers straight.
Vayu Mudra Helps in diseases like arthritis, trembling in Parkinson's disease. Better results obtained if practiced after Prana mudra. **Method** Press the index finger on the base of thumb and keep the thumb on the index finger. Let the other fingers be straight.
Prithvi Mudra Makes body sturdy. One experiences happiness. **Method** Join the tip of the thumb and ring finger.
Varun Mudra Improves the deteriorated quality of blood due to shortage of water & gives freshness to the body. **Method** Join the tip of the thumb and little finger. **Surya Mudra** Reduces weight of your body. **Method** Put the tip of ring finger at the base of thumb, with thumb gently pressing on it.
Ling Mudra Produces heat in the body and helps in curing cold and cough. **Method** Interlock the fingers of both hands together. Keeping the left thumb up (encircled by right thumb and index finger) i.e. left thumb should be vertically straight and right thumb around it.

TCM, Chinese Mudras

According to the theory of meridians in TCM the ten fingers are connected with the heart. Of the 12 meridian channels in the body, six are located in the hands and fingertips; the 3 yang and 3 yin meridians. By holding the hands and bending the fingers in a certain manner, usually connecting the thumb to the other fingers, you can regulate the Ch'i and its flow within these meridian channels.

There are several hand positions that help make mind-body connections within the meridians.

Thumb
Hand Tai-Yin of the lung meridian; has supportive effect on the respiratory system; enhances the rate of metabolism; helps relieve coughing, asthma, dry mouth, tightness in chest, shoulder and back pain.

Index finger
Hand Yang-Ming of large intestine meridian: has supportive effect on the liver, stomach, and large intestine; relieves loose bowels, stuffy nose, and laryngitis.

Middle finger
Hand Jai-Yin of exterior heart meridian: has supportive effect on regulation of blood vessels and circulatory system; helps control tachycardia, irregular heart palpitation, mental disturbances, and problems related to thorax membrane.

Ring finger
Hand Shan-Yang of triple heater meridian: has supportive effect on tuning of central nervous system, including eye and ear disorders and facial swelling.

Little finger
Hand Shao-Yin of heart meridian, hand Shao-Yang of small intestine meridian; has supportive effect on regulation of the urinary and reproductive systems hands including white spots in the eyes; helps relieve shoulder and lumbar pain.

The finger positions above are not the only interpretations of finger-lickin' elements. Practitioners of Polarity therapy designate the order to be:

Thumb	ether
Index finger	air
Middle finger	fire
Ring finger	water
Little finger	earth

It is really all about intention. Dogs without tails wag with their bodies. People without fingers and hands can still project powerfully effective intentionality. It is not the tool or the technique; it's the person--practitioner that is important.

Use whichever fingers you like. The quality and style of the intention you project can only come from you. You're the only one who has your tools and you're the only one knows how to use them!

Notes, thoughts, impressions...

LaVergne, TN USA
15 September 2009

157855LV00003B/3/P